Infinity Prime Donna Casey

"This fractal is a classic spiral, which is my favorite, and I'm always amazed at the variations and the endlessly repeating patterns that can be created out of such a primary shape." – **Donna Casey**

GRADE K

What Comes Next?

Patterns and Functions

UNIT 3

Investigations

IN NUMBER, DATA, AND SPACE®

Editorial offices: Glenview, Illinois • Parsippany, New Jersey • New York, New York
Sales offices: Boston, Massachusetts • Duluth, Georgia
Glenview, Illinois • Coppell, Texas • Sacramento, California • Mesa, Arizona

The Investigations curriculum was developed by TERC, Cambridge, MA.

This material is based on work supported by the National Science Foundation ("NSF") under Grant No. ESI-0095450. Any opinions, findings, and conclusions or recommendations expressed in this material are those of the author(s) and do not necessarily reflect the views of the National Science Foundation.

ISBN: 0-328-23722-1

ISBN: 978-0-328-23722-7

4 5 6 7 8 9 10-V003-15 14 13 12 11 10 09 08 07

CC:N1

Co-Principal Investigators

Susan Jo Russell

Karen Economopoulos

Authors

Lucy Wittenberg
Director Grades 3–5

Karen Economopoulos
Director Grades K–2

Virginia Bastable
(SummerMath for Teachers, Mt. Holyoke College)

Katie Hickey Bloomfield

Keith Cochran

Darrell Earnest

Arusha Hollister

Nancy Horowitz

Erin Leidl

Megan Murray

Young Oh

Beth W. Perry

Susan Jo Russell

Deborah Schifter
(Education Development Center)

Kathy Sillman

Administrative Staff

Amy Taber
Project Manager

Beth Bergeron

Lorraine Brooks

Emi Fujiwara

Contributing Authors

Denise Baumann

Jennifer DiBrienza

Hollee Freeman

Paula Hooper

Jan Mokros

Stephen Monk
(University of Washington)

Mary Beth O'Connor

Judy Storeygard

Cornelia Tierney

Elizabeth Van Cleef

Carol Wright

Technology

Jim Hammerman

Classroom Field Work

Amy Appell

Rachel E. Davis

Traci Higgins

Julia Thompson

Note: Unless otherwise noted, all contributors listed above were staff of the Education Research Collaborative at TERC during their work on the curriculum. Other affiliations during the time of development are listed.

Collaborating Teachers

This group of dedicated teachers carried out extensive field testing in their classrooms, met regularly to discuss issues of teaching and learning mathematics, provided feedback to staff, welcomed staff into their classrooms to document students' work, and contributed both suggestions and written material that has been incorporated into the curriculum.

Bethany Altchek
Linda Amaral
Kimberly Beauregard
Barbara Bernard
Nancy Buell
Rose Christiansen
Chris Colbath-Hess
Lisette Colon
Kim Cook
Frances Cooper
Kathleen Drew
Rebeka Eston Salemi
Thomas Fisher
Michael Flynn
Holly Ghazey
Susan Gillis
Danielle Harrington
Elaine Herzog
Francine Hiller
Kirsten Lee Howard
Liliana Klass
Leslie Kramer
Melissa Lee Andrichak
Kelley Lee Sadowski
Jennifer Levitan
Mary Lou LoVecchio
Kristen McEnaney
Maura McGrail
Kathe Millett
Florence Molyneaux
Amy Monkiewicz
Elizabeth Monopoli
Carol Murray
Robyn Musser
Christine Norrman
Deborah O'Brien
Timothy O'Connor
Anne Marie O'Reilly
Mark Paige
Margaret Riddle
Karen Schweitzer
Elisabeth Seyferth
Susan Smith
Debra Sorvillo
Shoshanah Starr
Janice Szymaszek
Karen Tobin
JoAnn Trauschke
Ana Vaisenstein
Yvonne Watson
Michelle Woods
Mary Wright

Advisors

Deborah Lowenberg Ball, University of Michigan

Hyman Bass, Professor of Mathematics and Mathematics Education University of Michigan

Mary Canner, Principal, Natick Public Schools

Thomas Carpenter, Professor of Curriculum and Instruction, University of Wisconsin-Madison

Janis Freckmann, Elementary Mathematics Coordinator, Milwaukee Public Schools

Lynne Godfrey, Mathematics Coach, Cambridge Public Schools

Ginger Hanlon, Instructional Specialist in Mathematics, New York City Public Schools

DeAnn Huinker, Director, Center for Mathematics and Science Education Research, University of Wisconsin-Milwaukee

James Kaput, Professor of Mathematics, University of Massachusetts-Dartmouth

Kate Kline, Associate Professor, Department of Mathematics and Statistics, Western Michigan University

Jim Lewis, Professor of Mathematics, University of Nebraska-Lincoln

William McCallum, Professior of Mathematics, University of Arizona

Harriet Pollatsek, Professor of Mathematics, Mount Holyoke College

Debra Shein-Gerson, Elementary Mathematics Specialist, Weston Public Schools

Gary Shevell, Assistant Principal, New York City Public Schools

Liz Sweeney, Elementary Math Department, Boston Public Schools

Lucy West, Consultant, Metamorphosis: Teaching Learning Communities, Inc.

This revision of the curriculum was built on the work of the many authors who contributed to the first edition (published between 1994 and 1998). We acknowledge the critical contributions of these authors in developing the content and pedagogy of *Investigations*:

Authors

Joan Akers

Michael T. Battista

Douglas H. Clements

Karen Economopoulos

Marlene Kliman

Jan Mokros

Megan Murray

Ricardo Nemirovsky

Andee Rubin

Susan Jo Russell

Cornelia Tierney

Contributing Authors

Mary Berle-Carman

Rebecca B. Corwin

Rebeka Eston

Claryce Evans

Anne Goodrow

Cliff Konold

Chris Mainhart

Sue McMillen

Jerrie Moffet

Tracy Noble

Kim O'Neil

Mark Ogonowski

Julie Sarama

Amy Shulman Weinberg

Margie Singer

Virginia Woolley

Tracey Wright

Contents

UNIT 3

What Comes Next?

Overview of Program Components

FOR TEACHERS

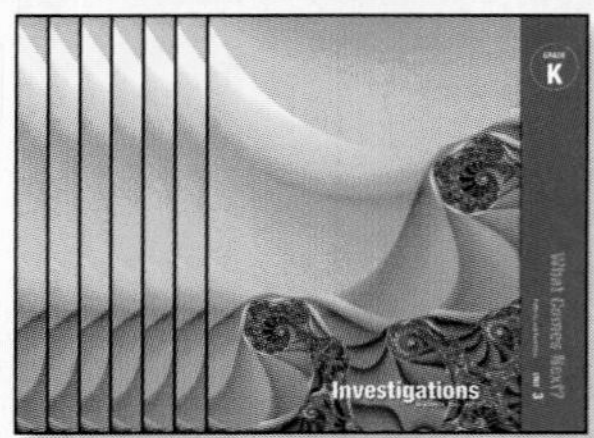

The **Curriculum Units** are the teaching guides. (See far right.)

Implementing Investigations in Kindergarten offers suggestions for implementing the curriculum. It also contains a comprehensive index.

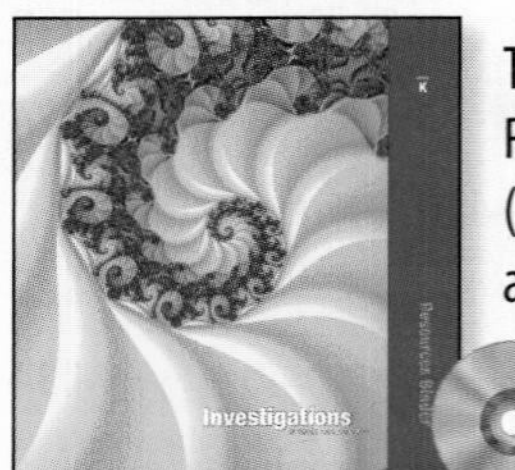

The **Resources Binder** contains all the Resource Masters that support instruction. (Also available on CD) The binder also includes a student software CD.

FOR STUDENTS

The **Student Activity Book** contains the consumable student pages (Recording Sheets, Homework, Practice, and so on).

The **Student Math Handbook Flip Chart** contains pictures of Math Words and Ideas pages.

The *Investigations* Curriculum

Investigations in Number, Data, and Space® is a K–5 mathematics curriculum designed to engage students in making sense of mathematical ideas. Six major goals guided the development of the *Investigations in Number, Data, and Space®* curriculum. The curriculum is designed to:

- Support students to make sense of mathematics and learn that they can be mathematical thinkers
- Focus on computational fluency with whole numbers as a major goal of the elementary grades
- Provide substantive work in important areas of mathematics—rational numbers, geometry, measurement, data, and early algebra—and connections among them
- Emphasize reasoning about mathematical ideas
- Communicate mathematics content and pedagogy to teachers
- Engage the range of learners in understanding mathematics

Underlying these goals are three guiding principles that are touchstones for the *Investigations* team as we approach both students and teachers as agents of their own learning:

1. *Students have mathematical ideas.* Students come to school with ideas about numbers, shapes, measurements, patterns, and data. If given the opportunity to learn in an environment that stresses making sense of mathematics, students build on the ideas they already have and learn about new mathematics they have never encountered. Students learn that they are capable of having mathematical ideas, applying what they know to new situations, and thinking and reasoning about unfamiliar problems.

2. *Teachers are engaged in ongoing learning* about mathematics content, pedagogy, and student learning. The curriculum provides material for professional development, to be used by teachers individually or in groups, that supports teachers' continued learning as they use the curriculum over several years. The *Investigations* curriculum materials are designed as much to be a dialogue with teachers as to be a core of content for students.

3. *Teachers collaborate with the students and curriculum materials* to create the curriculum as enacted in the classroom. The only way for a good curriculum to be used well is for teachers to be active participants in implementing it. Teachers use the curriculum to maintain a clear, focused, and coherent agenda for mathematics teaching. At the same time, they observe and listen carefully to students, try to understand how they are thinking, and make teaching decisions based on these observations.

Investigations is based on experience from research and practice, including field testing that involved documentation of thousands of hours in classrooms, observations of students, input from teachers, and analysis of student work. As a result, the curriculum addresses the learning needs of real students in a wide range of classrooms and communities. The investigations are carefully designed to invite all students into mathematics—girls and boys; members of diverse cultural, ethnic, and language groups; and students with a wide variety of strengths, needs, and interests.

Based on this extensive classroom testing, the curriculum takes seriously the time students need to develop a strong conceptual foundation and skills based on that foundation. Each curriculum unit focuses on an area of content in depth, providing time for students to develop and practice ideas across a variety of activities and contexts that build on each other. Daily guidelines for time spent on class sessions, Classroom Routines (K–3), and Ten-Minute Math (3–5) reflect the commitment to devoting adequate time to mathematics in each school day.

About This Curriculum Unit

This **Curriculum Unit** is one of seven teaching guides in Grade K. The third unit in Grade K is *What Comes Next?*

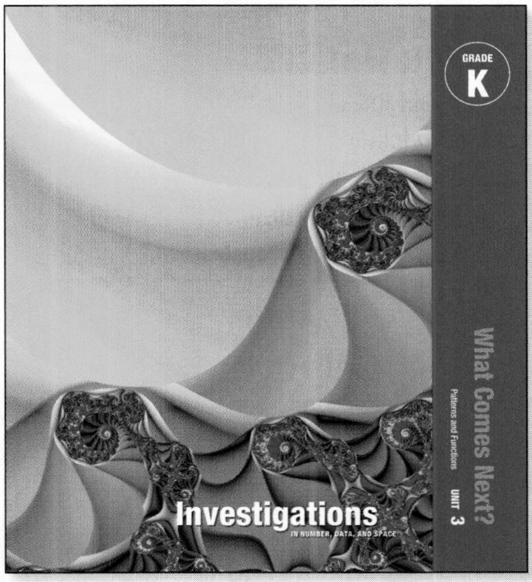

- The **Introduction and Overview** section organizes and presents the instructional materials, provides background information, and highlights important features specific to this unit.
- Each Curriculum Unit contains several **Investigations.** Each Investigation focuses on a set of related mathematical ideas.
- Investigations are divided into 30–45 minute **Sessions,** or lessons.
- Sessions have a combination of these parts: **Activity, Discussion, Math Workshop,** and **Session Follow-Up.**
- Each session also has one or more **Classroom Routines** that are done outside of math time.
- At the back of the book is a collection of **Teacher Notes** and **Dialogue Boxes** that provide professional development related to the unit.
- Also included at the back of the book are the **Student Math Handbook Flip Chart** pages for this unit.
- The **Index** provides a way to look up important words or terms.

Overview

OF THIS UNIT

<table>
<tr><th>Investigation</th><th>Session</th><th>Day</th></tr>
<tr><td rowspan="5">INVESTIGATION 1
What Do You Notice?
In an observation walk and a game called What's Missing?, students observe carefully, describe their surroundings, and identify missing objects. They copy and extend patterns using body motions and begin to distinguish between patterns and non-patterns as they construct trains of cubes.</td><td>1.1 Observation Walk</td><td>1</td></tr>
<tr><td>1.2 What's Missing?</td><td>2</td></tr>
<tr><td>1.3 Can You Do What I Do?</td><td>3</td></tr>
<tr><td>1.4 Two Kinds of Cube Trains</td><td>4</td></tr>
<tr><td>1.5 Cube Train Patterns</td><td>5</td></tr>
<tr><td rowspan="10">INVESTIGATION 2
Constructing Patterns
Students construct patterns using a variety of materials, including cubes, pattern blocks, tiles, and arrows, and record some of their patterns on paper. They also identify what comes next in patterns constructed by others.</td><td>2.1 Making Patterns</td><td>6</td></tr>
<tr><td>2.2 Patterns on the Pocket Chart</td><td>7</td></tr>
<tr><td>2.3 Recording Cube Train Patterns</td><td>8</td></tr>
<tr><td>2.4 Pattern Block Snakes</td><td>9</td></tr>
<tr><td>2.5 One-Two Patterns</td><td>10</td></tr>
<tr><td>2.6 What Comes Next?</td><td>11</td></tr>
<tr><td>2.7 Is It a Pattern?</td><td>12</td></tr>
<tr><td>2.8 Arrow Patterns</td><td>13</td></tr>
<tr><td>2.9 Add On</td><td>14</td></tr>
<tr><td>2.10 Sharing Patterns</td><td>15</td></tr>
<tr><td rowspan="7">INVESTIGATION 3
What's the Unit?
Students make patterns using a variety of materials and then break these patterns down into units. They also construct patterns from a given unit.</td><td>3.1 Break the Train</td><td>16</td></tr>
<tr><td>3.2 Recording Break the Train</td><td>17</td></tr>
<tr><td>3.3 How Many Cars?</td><td>18</td></tr>
<tr><td>3.4 Break the Train with Other Materials</td><td>19</td></tr>
<tr><td>3.5 12 Chips</td><td>20</td></tr>
<tr><td>3.6 End-of-Unit Assessment and Comparing Patterns</td><td>21</td></tr>
<tr><td>3.7 End-of-Unit Assessment and the Pattern Display</td><td>22</td></tr>
</table>

Each *Investigations* session has some combination of these four parts: **Activity, Discussion, Math Workshop,** and **Session Follow-Up.** These session parts are indicated in the chart below. Each session also has one or more **Classroom Routines** that are done outside of math time.

Activity	Discussion	Math Workshop	Assessment Checklist*	Session Follow-Up	Classroom Routines			
					Calendar	*Attendance*	*Today's Question*	*Patterns*
●●	●			●		●		
●●	●	●		●			●	
	●●	●		●	●			
●	●●●			●		●		
●	●●	●	●	●			●	
●	●●	●		●	●			
●	●	●		●		●		
●	●●	●		●			●	
●●	●●			●	●			
●	●	●		●		●		
●	●	●		●			●	
●	●	●		●				●
●	●	●		●				●
●●	●			●	●			
●●	●	●		●		●		
●●	●		●	●			●	
●	●	●		●				●
●	●	●		●	●			
●	●	●		●		●		
●●	●			●			●	
	●●	●		●				●
	●●	●		●	●			

*An Assessment Checklist is introduced in this session.

Mathematics

IN THIS UNIT

What Comes Next? is the third of seven units in the Kindergarten sequence and is the only Kindergarten unit in the patterns, functions, and change strand of *Investigations.* These units develop ideas about patterns, sequences, and functions and are part of the early algebra foundation integrated into the *Investigations* curriculum. The mathematical focus of this unit is on describing, extending, constructing, and recording repeating patterns; determining what comes next in a given pattern, and beginning to think about the structure of repeating patterns (i.e., a unit that is repeated over and over).

Students are not expected to have previous experience with patterns. This unit does build on *Who Is in School Today?,* where students explored many of the materials they will use in this unit and began thinking about attributes such as color, shape, size, and quantity.

This unit focuses on 3 Mathematical Emphases:

1 Data Analysis Sorting and classifying

Math Focus Points

- Finding objects that share one attribute
- Using attributes to sort a group of objects
- Comparing how objects are the same and different

In order to identify and construct repeating patterns, students must first be able to observe and to identify attributes. For example, when looking at an arrangement of pattern blocks, students must be able to see the attributes being used (e.g., shape, color, number, orientation) and the regularity in the way they are arranged. Therefore, the initial activities in this unit focus on careful observation, identifying different attributes, and using them to find a match or to sort a set of objects.

2 Repeating Patterns **Constructing, describing, and extending repeating patterns**

Math Focus Points

- Copying, constructing, comparing, describing, and recording repeating patterns
- Determining what comes next in a repeating pattern
- Comparing repeating and non-repeating arrangements
- Distinguishing between patterns and non-patterns
- Constructing a variety of patterns using the same elements
- Comparing different kinds of patterns

Students begin to appreciate the beauty and complexity of pattern as they identify patterns in the world around them, hear them in language and music, feel them in beats and motions, construct simple models and representations, and describe what they see and hear. Patterns are indeed everywhere, and there are many different kinds. In this unit, students construct, describe, extend, and determine what comes next in repeating patterns. Students encounter patterns with two (AB, AAB, ABB patterns) or three (ABC patterns) colors, shapes, arrows, quantities, or body motions.

When students are asked to describe a given pattern, they must decide which feature or features are most important. For example, many use color words to describe the following pattern.

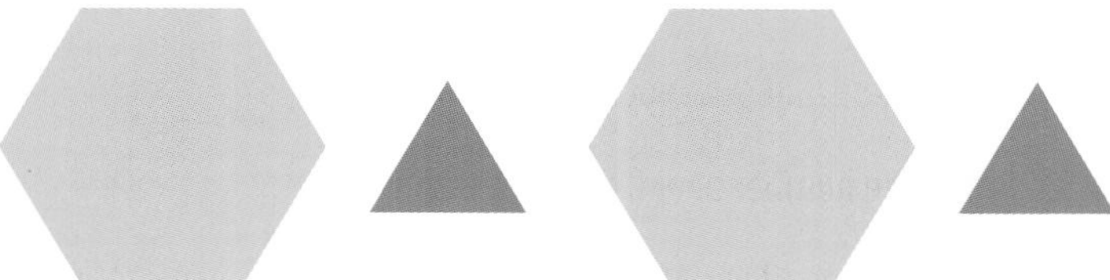

They will call it, "yellow, green, yellow, green." Others use shape names to describe it: "hexagon, triangle, hexagon, triangle." As students construct and describe many different patterns, they become more familiar with the structure of patterns and can begin to think how this pattern is both the same as and different from an AB pattern that alternates red trapezoids and orange squares.

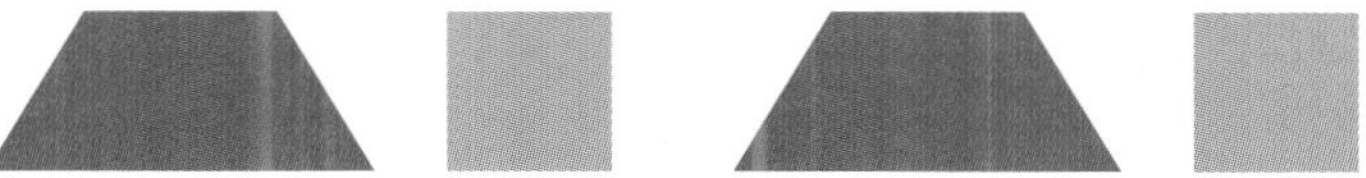

Although some students see that both patterns alternate two different elements, many kindergarteners see these patterns as unrelated because the most salient attributes of color and shape are different. Being able to identify the underlying similarity, that both are AB patterns, is an important idea in understanding patterns and will be a major focus of the pattern work in first grade.

3 Repeating Patterns **Identifying the unit of a repeating pattern**

Math Focus Points

- Identifying the unit of a repeating pattern
- Counting the number of units in a repeating pattern
- Extending a repeating pattern by adding on units to the pattern

In this unit, students describe, construct, extend, and record repeating patterns. The activities in Investigation 3 focus students' attention on analyzing the structure of a repeating pattern by identifying the *unit* of the pattern—the part of the pattern that repeats over and over. For example, in the pattern sequence a–b–a–b–a–b, the unit is AB. Repetitions of this unit, one after the other, make a pattern.

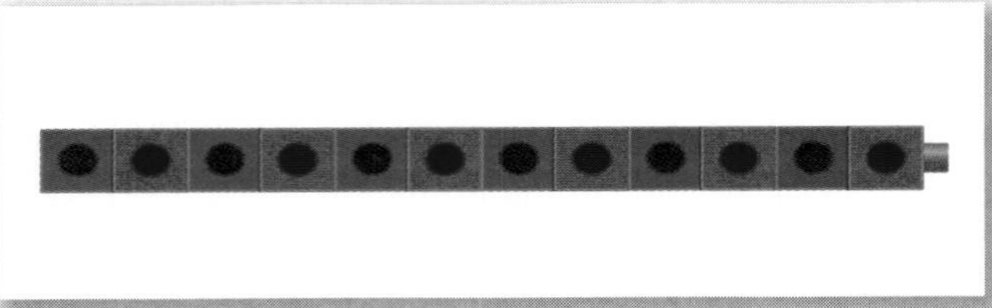

As units get larger and more complex, it is sometimes difficult to look at a pattern and figure out the basic unit. The pattern sequence a–b–b–a–b–b–a–b–b has a 3-element unit: ABB. However, the unit of the pattern sequence a–b–b–a–a–b–b–a–a–b–b–a is harder to see. This pattern shows three repetitions of the basic unit ABBA.

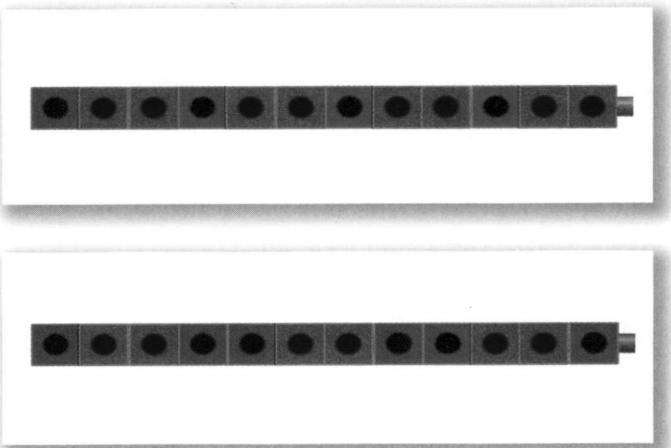

Although some students can easily describe the unit of a pattern, many begin by thinking only in terms of "what comes after what." That is, for the cube sequence blue–red–blue–red–blue–red, students won't necessarily think about the pattern as being made from the unit blue–red. Rather, they will think of the pattern as "red comes after blue, blue comes after red." They think about the action of building a sequence in order to understand the pattern. Through repeated opportunities to break patterns into units and to construct patterns using a given unit, most students by the end of this unit will be able to identify the unit of a pattern.

This Unit also focuses on

- Observing and describing
- Using information to figure out what is missing
- Counting, creating, and representing quantities
- Counting 12 objects

Classroom Routines focus on

- Developing strategies for counting accurately
- Considering whether order matters when you count
- Comparing quantities
- Using the calendar as a tool for keeping track of time
- Collecting, counting, representing, describing, and comparing data
- Determining what comes next in a repeating pattern
- Describing repeating patterns

This unit raises students' awareness of pattern and regularity. Much of mathematics is about noticing and describing patterns and regularities that occur in the relationships among mathematical objects—numbers and shapes, for example. Once students begin looking for and expecting patterns in mathematics, they become alert to regularities that can help them understand important mathematical relationships.

The experiences in this unit lay the foundation for later work with pattern in number and geometry, in Kindergarten and throughout the elementary years. In particular, the Grade 1 patterns and functions unit, *Color, Shape, and Number Patterns,* revisits repeating patterns and introduces situations with a constant increase. The focus of students' work with repeating patterns is on constructing, describing, and comparing patterns; on identifying the unit of various patterns; and on connecting repeating patterns to the number sequence (e.g., determining what color the 15th cube would be if an 8-cube AB pattern were continued). The work with constant increase focuses on contexts (e.g., a penny jar or sets of staircases) that result in a sequence of numbers (e.g., 2, 4, 6, 8) that students then consider.

Assessment

IN THIS UNIT

Every session in this unit provides an opportunity for Ongoing Assessment. In addition, assessment checklists are provided to keep track of your observations about students' work with concepts and ideas that are benchmarks for this unit.

ONGOING ASSESSMENT: Observing Students at Work

The following sessions provide **Ongoing Assessment: Observing Students at Work** opportunities:

- **Session 1.1, p. 28**
- **Session 1.2, pp. 32 and 33**
- **Session 1.3, p. 37**
- **Session 1.4, p. 42**
- **Session 1.5, p. 47**
- **Session 2.1, pp. 61 and 62**
- **Session 2.2, p. 68**
- **Session 2.3, p. 73**
- **Session 2.4, p. 78**
- **Session 2.5, p. 83**
- **Session 2.6, p. 87**
- **Session 2.7, p. 92**
- **Session 2.8, p. 97**
- **Session 2.9, p. 101**
- **Session 3.1, p. 117**
- **Session 3.2, pp. 120 and 121**
- **Session 3.3, p. 127**
- **Session 3.4, p. 131**
- **Session 3.5, p. 136**

WRITING OPPORTUNITIES

The following sessions have **writing** opportunities for students to explain their mathematical thinking:

- **Sessions 1.3, 1.5, and 2.1, pp. 37, 48, and 62**
  Counting Jar
- **Sessions 2.3–2.8, pp. 73, 78, 83, 88, 93, and 97**
  Recording Patterns
- **Sessions 3.1–3.4, pp. 117, 120, 127, 131**
  Student Activity Book, p. 22
  M18, *Break the Train* Recording Sheet
- **Sessions 3.2–3.4, pp. 121, 127, and 132**
  Counting Jar

PORTFOLIO OPPORTUNITIES

The following sessions have work appropriate for a **portfolio:**

- **Sessions 1.3, 1.5, and 2.1, pp. 37, 48, and 62**
  Counting Jar
- **Session 2.10, p. 105**
  Choosing a Favorite Pattern
- **Sessions 3.1–3.4, pp. 117, 120, 127, 131**
  Student Activity Book, p. 22
  M18, *Break the Train:* Recording Sheet
- **Sessions 3.2–3.4, pp. 121, 127, and 132**
  Counting Jar
- **Sessions 3.5–3.7, pp. 135, 140, and 145**
  Student Activity Book, p. 24
  M20, 12 Chips

Assessing the Benchmarks

Observing students as they engage in conversation about their ideas is a primary means to assess their mathematical understanding. Consider all of your students' work, not just the written assessments. See the chart below for suggestions about key activities to observe.

Assessment Checklists are introduced in Session 1.5 and Session 3.1. Use these checklists to determine which students need to complete an End-of-Unit Assessment interview. Over the course of Sessions 3.6 and 3.7, meet individually with students who have not yet clearly met each benchmark or about whom you have questions.

Benchmarks in This Unit	Key Activities to Observe	Assessment
1. Copy, construct, and extend simple repeating patterns, such as AB, ABC.	**Session 2.1:** Making Patterns **Session 2.3:** Recording Cube Train Patterns **Session 2.6:** What Comes Next? **Session 2.9:** Add On	**Session 1.5:** Assessment Checklist: Repeating Patterns ✓
2. Begin to identify the unit of a repeating pattern.	**Session 3.1:** *Break the Train* **Session 3.3:** *How Many Cars?*	**Session 3.1:** Assessment Checklist: Identifying the Unit of a Pattern ✓

Relating the Mathematical Emphases to the Benchmarks

Mathematical Emphases	Benchmarks
Data Analysis Sorting and classifying	
Repeating Patterns Constructing, describing, and extending repeating patterns	1
Repeating Patterns Identifying the unit of a repeating pattern	2

Algebra Connections

IN THIS UNIT

This essay is intended to illustrate how the ideas your students engage with in this unit lay the foundation for algebra. *What Comes Next?* is the very first unit in the Patterns, Functions, and Change strand of the *Investigations* curriculum. Students are embarking on a series of activities that progress through the grades, gradually moving from describing color, shape, and movement patterns constructed from a repeating unit to connecting these patterns to number sequences, and, finally, to describing functions based on these sequences.

Consider this scene in a Kindergarten classroom. The students are comparing two cube trains made with 8 connecting cubes. The color sequence of the first cube train is red–blue–yellow–brown–white–green–yellow–orange. The color sequence of the second cube train is red–yellow–red–yellow–red–yellow–red–yellow.

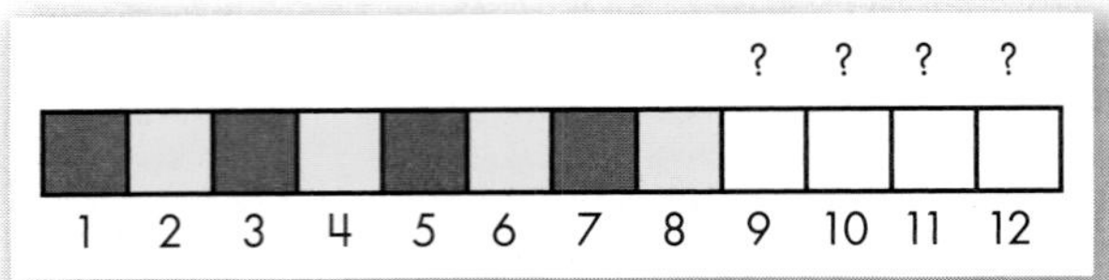

After some students describe each train, the teacher asks them what is the same or different about the two trains.

Tammy: That one is like a rainbow. It has every color.

Raul: It doesn't have every color, but it's pretty. The other one is a candy cane.

Cindy: It's striped like my shirt.

Jason: That one has lots of colors. That one has just red and yellow. It's a pattern.

Teacher: What do you mean that it's a pattern? Who can say what Jason might be thinking about?

Emma: It goes red yellow red yellow red yellow. It just keeps going over and over.

Mia: The other one isn't a pattern. It's just any colors.

Teacher: There are a lot of different kinds of patterns. We're going to be learning about repeating patterns in the next few weeks—patterns that, like Emma said, keep going over and over.

In this class, students are just beginning to consider repeating patterns. In this unit, students construct and describe AB and ABC color patterns made with connecting cubes. They answer questions about what comes next in a repeating pattern such as the red–yellow sequence. If this red–yellow pattern continues in the same way, what color is next? A Kindergarten student might say, "Red comes after yellow and yellow comes after red. I know red has to come next."

In Grade 1, students continue to answer questions about "what comes next," and also consider questions about what comes in a later position in the repeating sequence. Numbering the red–yellow pattern with the counting numbers makes it easier to pose problems such as, "If this pattern continues in the same way, what color will the 12th cube be?"

In Kindergarten, students also consider how a repeating pattern is constructed out of a sequence of units. For example, the pattern shown here can be constructed from a repeating red–yellow unit. In Grades 1 and 2, students notice that certain elements of the unit are described by a particular number sequence. For example, a student might say, "I know that the 12th cube is yellow because all the even numbers are yellow." This student is noticing something about the structure of the 2-element unit. The first element in each unit, which is always red, falls on the numbers 1, 3, 5, 7, 9, . . . The second element in each unit, yellow, falls on the numbers 2, 4, 6, 8, 10, . . .

In Grades 1 and 2 the overall position of a particular yellow cube in the red–yellow sequence can be described in this way: the 1st yellow cube is in position 2, the 2nd yellow cube is in position 4, the 7th yellow cube is in position 14, and so forth. Students encounter a variety of situations in which there is a correspondence from one set of values to another. For example, if a building has 2 rooms per floor, there is a correspondence between the number of floors and the total number of rooms. If one puts 2 pennies in a jar each day, there is a correspondence between the number of days one has been doing this and the total number of pennies in the jar. In a red–yellow repeating pattern that is numbered with the counting numbers, there is a correspondence between the position of a yellow cube among the yellow cubes (e.g., the 3rd yellow cube) and its position in the entire sequence (e.g., the 6th cube).

Building with 2 rooms per floor		**Jar with 2 pennies per day**		**Repeating pattern with red–yellow unit**	
Number of floors	Total no. of rooms	Number of days	Total no. of pennies	Number of yellows	Number of cubes
1	2	1	2	1	2
2	4	2	4	2	4
3	6	3	6	3	6
4	8	4	8	4	8
5	10	5	10	5	10
6	12	6	12	6	12
7	14	7	14	7	14
8	16	8	16	8	16

Note that all three contexts generate the same table of values. In any of these contexts, students can work with the relationship between the two variables as they solve problems such as:

- How many rooms in a building with 20 floors?
- How many pennies in the jar after 35 days?
- In a red–yellow repeating pattern that is numbered with the counting numbers, what is the number of the 100th yellow cube?

Students eventually work to find general rules that describe the correspondence from one set to another. To find the position of any yellow cube in a red–yellow sequence, a student might say:

If you multiply the number of the yellow cube by 2, you get its position.

This rule can also be expressed with algebraic notation, which students encounter in Grade 4:

> $y = 2x$, where y is the position of the cube in the entire sequence and x is its position among the yellow cubes

This same rule describes the floor-room relationship shown in the table, where x is the number of floors and y is the total number of rooms, and it describes the penny jar situation shown in the table, where x is the number of days and y is the number of pennies in the jar.

In Kindergarten, as students describe repeating patterns, they are at the beginning of looking for, describing, and analyzing regularities in mathematics. For most adults, notation (the use of variables, operations, and equal signs) is the chief identifying feature of algebra. The notation expresses, in equations, rules satisfied by particular pairs of quantities. Students in Kindergarten describe repeating patterns in their own ways and begin to understand regularities in structure that they can later describe with numbers and equations. This *reasoning*—about what the mathematical relationship is—*not* the notation, is the central work of elementary students in algebra.

Classroom Routines

IN THIS UNIT

Classroom Routines offer practice and review of key concepts for this grade level. These daily activities, to be done in 10 minutes outside of math class, occur in a regular rotation every 4–5 days. Specific directions for the day's routine are provided in each session. For the full description and variations of each classroom routine, see *Implementing Investigations in Kindergarten.*

Attendance

Students continue to count to determine the total number of students present and to explore what happens when the count begins with different students. In order to help students connect the counting numbers to the quantities they represent, the class discusses how many students have counted midway through the count. Students also compare two groups, determine which group has more, and determine how many more there are in this larger group.

Math Focus Points

- Developing strategies for counting accurately
- Considering whether order matters when you count
- Comparing quantities

Calendar

Students continue to review the numbers and counting sequence to 31 and the names and sequence of the days of the week. Students also use the calendar to determine how many days until (or since) a special event and explain their strategies.

Math Focus Points

- Using the calendar as a tool for keeping track of time
- Developing strategies for counting accurately

Today's Question

Students record their response to a survey question with two possible answers on a two-column table. Class discussion focuses on describing and interpreting the data.

Math Focus Points

- Collecting, counting, representing, describing, and comparing data

Patterns on the Pocket Chart

Students see part of a repeating pattern. They describe and extend the pattern, determining what would come next if the pattern were to continue.

Math Focus Points

- Determining what comes next in a repeating pattern
- Describing repeating patterns

Practice and Review

IN THIS UNIT

Practice and review play a critical role in the *Investigations* program. The following components and features are available to provide regular reinforcement of key mathematical concepts and procedures.

Books	Features	In This Unit . . .
Curriculum Unit	**Classroom Routines** offer practice and review of key concepts for this grade level. These daily activities, to be done in ten minutes outside of math class, occur in a regular rotation every 4–5 days. Specific directions for the day's routine are provided in each session. For the full description and variations of each classroom routine see *Implementing Investigations in Kindergarten.*	• **All sessions**
Student Activity Book	**Practice** pages in the *Student Activity Book* provide one of two types of written practice: **reinforcement** of the content of the unit or **enrichment** opportunities.	• **Session 1.2** • **Session 2.6** • **Session 3.4** • **Session 3.6**
	Homework pages in the *Student Activity Book* are an extension of the work done in class. At times they help students prepare for upcoming activities.	• **Session 2.1**
Student Math Handbook Flip Chart	**Math Words and Ideas** in the *Student Math Handbook Flip Chart* are pages that summarize key words and ideas. Most Words and Ideas pages have at least one exercise.	• **Student Math Handbook Flip Chart, pp. 39, 40, 41, 42, 43, 48**

Supporting the Range of Learners

Sessions	1.2	1.3	1.4	1.5	2.1	2.2	2.3	2.4	2.5	2.6	2.7	2.8	2.9	2.10	3.1	3.2	3.3	3.4	3.5	3.7
Intervention	•		•	•	•	•	•	•	•	•	•	•	•			•	•		•	
Extension		•			•	•	•		•	•	•			•			•	•		
ELL	•	•						•							•					•

Intervention

Suggestions are made to support and engage students who are having difficulty with a particular idea, activity, or problem.

Extension

Suggestions are made to support and engage students who finish early or may be ready for additional challenge.

English Language Learners (ELL)

In this unit, students learn to describe, extend, construct, and record repeating patterns. The visual, tactile nature of the activities will help make these concepts accessible to English Language Learners. You can provide additional support by previewing or reviewing certain activities and emphasizing key vocabulary in context.

To succeed in this unit, English Language Learners must understand sequential vocabulary such as *first, next, then,* and *after.* You can demonstrate these terms as you construct a simple pattern. Watch as I make a pattern with red and blue cubes. *First,* I'll put a red cube. *Next,* I'll put a blue cube. *Then,* I'll put another red cube. What color should I put *after* the red cube? What color comes *after* that? You can assess students' understanding by encouraging them to think aloud as they construct their own patterns.

As they learn to identify smaller units with patterns, English Language Learners must understand positional words such as *next to* and *between.* Have students stand in a line to demonstrate this vocabulary. Mia, please stand here. Ricardo, please stand *next* to Mia. Yoshio, can you stand *between* Mia and Ricardo? Students can practice using these terms by giving each other similar commands. Then help English Language Learners apply these words to an AB pattern. Watch as I make a train with yellow and green squares. First, I'll put a yellow square. Then I'll put a green square *next* to the yellow square. Then I'll put another yellow square and another green square *next to* those. Ask a student to extend the pattern. Now let's break this train into cars. Let's put a toothpick *between* each of the cars. Where should we put the first toothpick? *Next to* the first green square? That's right. Let's put it *between* the first two cars of the train.

Working with the Range of Learners: Classroom Cases is a set of episodes written by teachers that focuses on meeting the needs of the range of learners in the classroom. In the first section, *Setting up the Mathematical Community,* teachers write about how they create a supportive and productive learning environment in their classrooms. In the next section, *Accommodations for Learning,* teachers focus on specific modifications they make to meet the needs of some of their learners. In the last section, *Language and Representation,* teachers share how they help students use representations and develop language to investigate and express mathematical ideas. The questions at the end of each case provide a starting point for your own reflection or for discussion with colleagues. See *Implementing Investigations in Kindergarten* for this set of episodes.

INVESTIGATION 1

Mathematical Emphases

Data Analysis Sorting and classifying

Math Focus Points

- Finding objects that share one attribute
- Using attributes to sort a group of objects
- Comparing how objects are the same and different

Repeating Patterns Constructing, describing, and extending repeating patterns

Math Focus Points

- Copying, constructing, comparing, describing, and recording repeating patterns
- Determining what comes next in a repeating pattern
- Comparing repeating and non-repeating arrangements
- Comparing different kinds of patterns

This Investigation also focuses on

- Observing and describing
- Using information to figure out what is missing
- Counting, creating, and representing quantities

What Do You Notice?

	Student Activity Book	Student Math Handbook Flip Chart	Professional Development: Read Ahead of Time	
SESSION 1.1 p. 26				
Observation Walk The class goes on a walk around the school or neighborhood to observe and describe their surroundings.			• **Mathematics in This Unit**, p. 10	
SESSION 1.2 p. 29				
What's Missing? Students learn *What's Missing?*, a game that involves identifying what's been removed from an array of objects. They revisit two attribute activities, *Button Match-Up* and Sorting Attribute Blocks.	18			
SESSION 1.3 p. 35				
Can You Do What I Do? Students copy a pattern that the teacher makes with hand and body motions. A new Counting Jar is added to Math Workshop. Class discussion focuses on how two buttons are the same and different.		39, 48	• **Teacher Note:** Repeating Patterns, p. 147	

Classroom Routines See page 18 for an overview.

Attendance

- **No materials needed**

Today's Question

- ***Today's Question* charts for Sessions 1.2 and 1.5. See instructions on pages 29 and 45.**

Calendar

- **Pocket calendar or classroom calendar**

Materials to Gather	Materials to Prepare
• **A book about observing** such as *I Am Eyes, Ni Macho; Brown Bear, Brown Bear, What Do You See?;* or *I Went Walking* (optional) • **Clipboard** (1 per student, optional)	• **M1, Family Letter** Make copies. (1 per student) • **Chart paper** Write the title, "What did you notice?"
• **Buttons** (1 bin per pair)	• ***What's Missing?* gameboards** Use masking tape or wide-tip markers to split a tray, piece of cardboard, or sheet of construction paper into nine sections. Make 4–5 boards. • ***What's Missing?* collections** Place nine small, related objects in a paper bag. Two examples are collections of art supplies (crayons, markers, scissors, paintbrushes) or things from nature (acorns, shells, rocks, sticks, seeds). Make 4–5 collections. • **M2, Attribute Cards** You can use the cards you made in Unit 1, or you can make new ones (as needed). Cut apart the cards and use crayons or markers to make the color words the appropriate color. If you are using half-sets of attribute blocks, make four sets and remove the thick and thin cards. If you are using full sets, make two complete sets of cards. • **Attribute blocks** Divide into half sets—one thin, one thick (to eliminate thickness as an attribute).
• **Materials for the Counting Jar activity** (as you have set it up) • **2 buttons** that have obvious similarities and differences • **Materials for *What's Missing?*** See Session 1.2. • **Materials for *Button Match-Up*** See Session 1.2. • **Materials for Sorting Attribute Block**s See Session 1.2.	• **Counting Jar** Place seven cubes or counters in the jar. • **Chart paper** Draw two buttons that have obvious similarities and differences.

What Do You Notice?, *continued*

	Student Activity Book	Student Math Handbook Flip Chart	Professional Development: Read Ahead of Time	
SESSION 1.4 p. 40				
Two Kinds of Cube Trains Students compare two cube trains—one with colors in a repeating pattern and one with assorted colors in a non-repeating arrangement—and try to determine what color comes next. Students then make their own cube trains and, as a whole class, sort the trains into two groups.		40	• **Dialogue Boxes:** Two Arrangements of Color, p. 155; Sharing Our Cube Trains, p. 157; What Might Come Next?, p. 159	
SESSION 1.5 p. 45				
Cube Train Patterns Students construct patterns with 8–10 cubes. Math Workshop focuses on constructing patterns and using attributes. Class discussion focuses on comparing different cube train patterns.		40	• **Teacher Note:** Assessment: Repeating Patterns, p. 149	

Materials to Gather	Materials to Prepare
• **Connecting cubes** (class set)	• **Two 8-cube trains** Make one with two colors in an alternating AB pattern and one with assorted colors in a non-repeating arrangement.
• **Cube train patterns** (from Session 1.4) • **Connecting cubes** (class set) • **Materials for Counting Jar** See Session 1.3. • **Materials for *What's Missing?*** See Session 1.2. • **Materials for *Button Match-Up*** See Session 1.2. • **Materials for Sorting Attribute Blocks** See Session 1.2.	• **M3, Assessment Checklist: Repeating Patterns** ✓ Make copies. (3–4 per class, plus extras as needed) • **Cube train patterns** Collect 4–5 different patterns students made during Session 1.4.

✓ Checklist Available

Observation Walk

Math Focus Points

- Observing and describing

Vocabulary

observe

Today's Plan		Materials
1 ACTIVITY **Introducing an Observation Walk**	5 MIN CLASS	• A book about observing (optional)
2 ACTIVITY **Observation Walk**	15–30 MIN CLASS	• Clipboard (optional)
3 DISCUSSION **What Did You Notice?**	10 MIN CLASS	• Chart: "What did you notice?"*
4 SESSION FOLLOW-UP **Homework**		• M1, Family Letter*

*See *Materials to Prepare,* p. 23.

Classroom Routines

Attendance: How Many Have Counted? **Count around the circle as usual but pause several times during the count to ask students how many people have counted so far and how they know. Help students see why the numbers they say represent the numbers of students who have counted so far and that the last number represents the total number of students in class today.**

ACTIVITY

Introducing an Observation Walk

5 MIN CLASS

Explain that you are beginning a new math unit that will ask students to look very carefully at things.①

Today we are going to take an observation walk. When you observe, you look very carefully. As we walk, use your eyes and look carefully at what is around you. Try to notice as much as you can. There may be things you have never noticed before. You will have a chance to share what you notice after the walk.②

ACTIVITY

Observation Walk

15–30 MIN CLASS

Take students on an observation walk around the classroom, school, playground, or neighborhood. As you walk, focus students' attention on specific things and encourage them to point out what they are noticing. Although the main purpose of this walk is for students to simply look carefully at their environment, it is a good opportunity to recognize patterns as well. Therefore, point out interesting arrangements of objects or patterns that appear in the surroundings.③

Students take an observation walk.

Teaching Notes

① **Children's Literature** Some teachers introduce this idea by reading a book about being observant and noticing the surroundings. Examples include *I Am Eyes, Ni Macho* by Leila Ward, *Brown Bear, Brown Bear, What Do You See?* by Bill Martin Jr., or *I Went Walking* by Sue Williams.

② **Recording and Sketching Observations** Take a blank piece of paper and a clipboard on the walk so you can record students' observations. These notes will inform the discussion later. Some teachers give each student a blank piece of paper and a clipboard for sketching something they notice. Others ask children to do this after they return.

Math Note

③ **Observing and Patterns** The purpose of the walk and the *What's Missing* activity in the next session is for students to observe carefully. In order to identify a pattern, students must be able to look carefully at, for example, a set of pattern blocks to identify the attributes (e.g., color and shape) and to consider how the blocks in question are arranged (e.g., red trapezoid, yellow hexagon, red trapezoid, yellow hexagon).

ONGOING ASSESSMENT: Observing Students at Work

Students look carefully at their surroundings and point out what they notice.

- **What do students notice?** How do they describe what they see? Do they notice any patterns? How do they name and describe them?

10 MIN CLASS

DISCUSSION

What Did You Notice?

Math Focus Points for Discussion

- Observing and describing

After taking an observation walk and giving students a few minutes to sketch something they noticed, bring them together to share their observations. Use the list you made while on the walk to prompt their memories as necessary. On the chart titled "What did you notice?," make a list of their observations, with simple sketches to illustrate each.

Students discuss what they noticed from their observation walk.

SESSION FOLLOW-UP

Homework

Family Letter: Send home copies of the Family Letter (M1).

What's Missing?

Math Focus Points

- Using information to figure out what is missing
- Finding objects that share one attribute
- Using attributes to sort a group of objects

Today's Plan			Materials
1 ACTIVITY **Introducing *What's Missing?***	5–10 MIN	CLASS	• *What's Missing?* gameboards*; *What's Missing?* collections*
2 ACTIVITY **Reintroducing Activities About Attributes**	5 MIN	CLASS	• M2* • Buttons; attribute blocks*
3 MATH WORKSHOP **Missing and Matching** 3A *What's Missing?* 3B *Button Match-Up* 3C Sorting Attribute Blocks	15–25 MIN		3A • *What's Missing?* gameboard; *What's Missing?* collection 3B • Buttons 3C • Attribute blocks; Attribute Cards*
4 DISCUSSION **Checking In**	5 MIN	CLASS	
5 SESSION FOLLOW-UP **Practice**			• *Student Activity Book,* p. 18

*See *Materials to Prepare,* p. 23.

Classroom Routines

Today's Question: Are you wearing the color blue today? **On chart paper, create a vertical two-column table titled, "Are you wearing the color blue today?" with "Yes" written at the bottom of one column and "No" written at the bottom of the other column. Students respond by writing their names above the appropriate choice. Count the responses as a class and discuss what the results of the survey tell you.**

ACTIVITY

Introducing *What's Missing?*

5–10 MIN CLASS

Show students the different *What's Missing?* collections you made and choose one student to demonstrate the game. Arrange the objects on a gameboard. Ask students what they notice about the set of objects.

A tray set up to play What's Missing?

Look very carefully at my tray. I am going to take one or two objects away and put them in this paper bag. Your job is to figure out what I took away.

After students have had an opportunity to look closely at the items on the tray (about one minute), ask them to cover their eyes. Remove one or two objects, and place them in the paper bag.

Take another look at my tray. What's missing? How do you know?

Students might say:

"There was a ball. Now there is not a ball."

"All the things were red. There was a red crayon. Now it is gone."

After discussing what other objects are missing and sharing different strategies for figuring it out, explain that students will play *What's Missing?* in pairs or groups of three later on during Math Workshop. Use volunteers to model how this will work, with the role of "hider" rotating each round. Emphasize that students should use the same set of objects, arranged in the same way, until each person has had a chance to be the hider.

ACTIVITY

Reintroducing Activities About Attributes

5 MIN CLASS

Students were introduced to *Button Match-Up* and Sorting Attribute Blocks in *Who Is in School Today?* (Unit 1). Briefly reintroduce them by playing a sample round with students.

In *Button Match-Up,* one player chooses a button. Students then work together to find buttons that match the chosen button. A match is made when buttons have at least one attribute in common.

In Sorting Attribute Blocks, students choose a card (e.g., BIG) from Attribute Cards (M2) and then work together to find all of the [BIG] blocks. ①

MATH WORKSHOP

Missing and Matching

15–25 MIN

Explain that the following three activities are available during Math Workshop. Remind students what each activity entails, what materials are required, and where they are located.

What's Missing?

PAIRS GROUPS

Students take turns removing one or two items from an array of nine and identifying the missing object(s).

Math Note

① **Attributes and Patterns** These activities help students identify attributes (e.g., size) and learn to pay attention to one while ignoring the rest (e.g., color, shape, thickness). As students identify and create patterns, they will use this crucial skill in order to pay attention to which attribute is repeating.

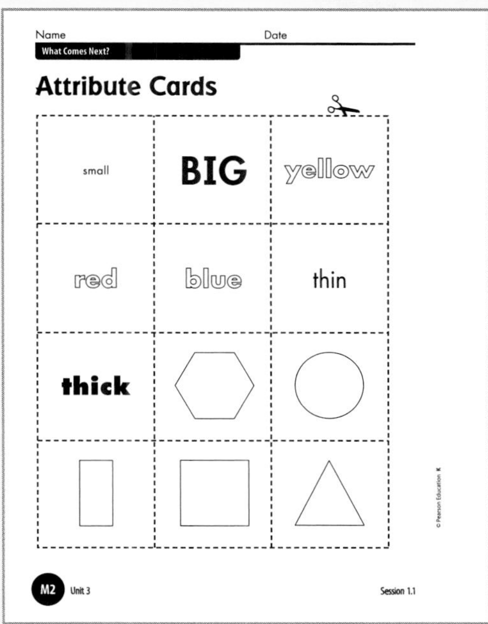

Name Date

What Comes Next?

Attribute Cards

small	BIG	yellow
red	blue	thin
thick		

M2 Unit 3 Session 1.1

▲ Resource Masters, M2

ONGOING ASSESSMENT: Observing Students at Work

Students look carefully at an arrangement of objects and identify what is missing when objects are removed.

- **What strategies do students use to figure out the missing object(s)?**
- **Do students attend to attributes, such as the size, shape, color, or function of objects, to help them determine what is missing?**
- **Do they use position or proximity?**
- **Can students explain their reasoning, logic, or strategies for determining what is missing?**

DIFFERENTIATION: Supporting the Range of Learners

Intervention Some students may benefit from playing with a smaller set of objects, perhaps two rows of three. Play in a small group with these students. Encourage them to describe what they see before any objects are removed. Remove only one object at a time, and encourage students to think aloud and help one another develop strategies for remembering where each object belongs.

ELL Some English Language Learners may have trouble participating fully in this game because they lack vocabulary knowledge. As students set up their boards, review the names of the objects in the collections.

I see a button, a bean, and a penny in the first row of your collection. Mia, what do you see in the second row?

Encourage English Language Learners and their native English-speaking partners to say the name of each object as they place it on the board.

3B *Button Match-Up*

Students work in pairs to find buttons that have at least one attribute in common.

ONGOING ASSESSMENT: Observing Students at Work

Students identify attributes and find objects that share at least one attribute.

- **Are students able to find buttons that share an attribute?** Can they explain how their buttons are the same? What language do they use?
- **As they play, do students focus exclusively on one attribute (e.g., color)?** Or, do they match buttons according to various attributes (e.g., size, shape, color, number of holes, type of material)?

DIFFERENTIATION: Supporting the Range of Learners

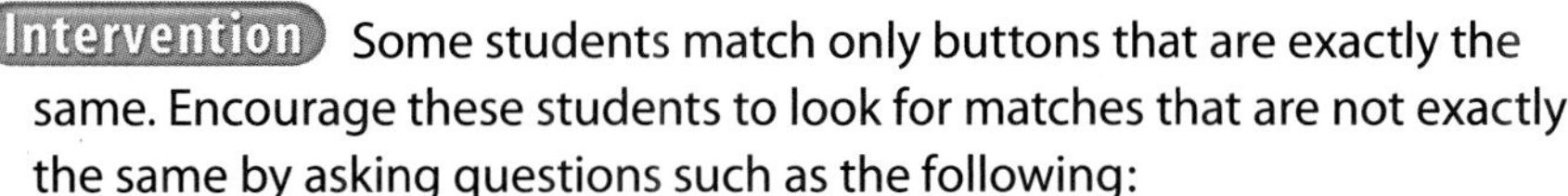

Intervention Some students match only buttons that are exactly the same. Encourage these students to look for matches that are not exactly the same by asking questions such as the following:

In what other ways do these buttons match?

Can you find another button that has two holes but isn't small, like this one?

How do these buttons match even though one is big and one is small?

3C Sorting Attribute Blocks

PAIRS

Pairs take turns picking an attribute card and working together to sort the attribute blocks according to the attribute on the card.

ONGOING ASSESSMENT: Observing Students at Work

Students sort objects according to their attributes.

- **Can students tell what attribute is shown on the card?** Can they find blocks with that attribute? Are students more confident with some attributes (for example color, but not shape)?
- **How clearly can students communicate about the attributes and the blocks under consideration?** What language do they use?
- **Do students try to find all of the blocks that fit a given attribute?** How do they know and/or explain that they have them all?

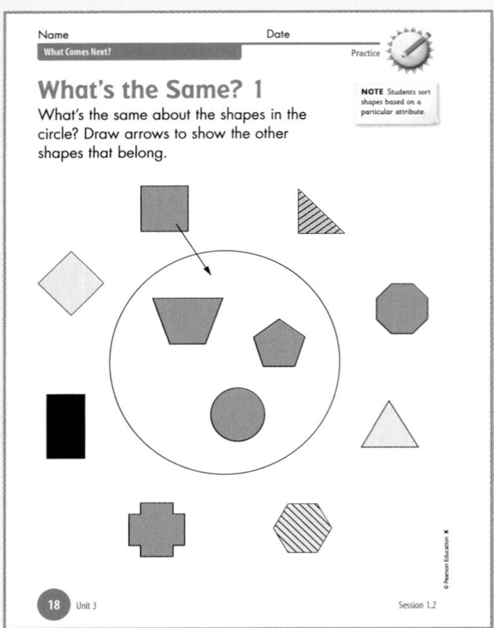

Name Date

What Comes Next? Practice

What's the Same? 1

What's the same about the shapes in the circle? Draw arrows to show the other shapes that belong.

NOTE Students sort shapes based on a particular attribute.

18 Unit 3 Session 1.2

© Pearson Education K

▲ Student Activity Book, p. 18

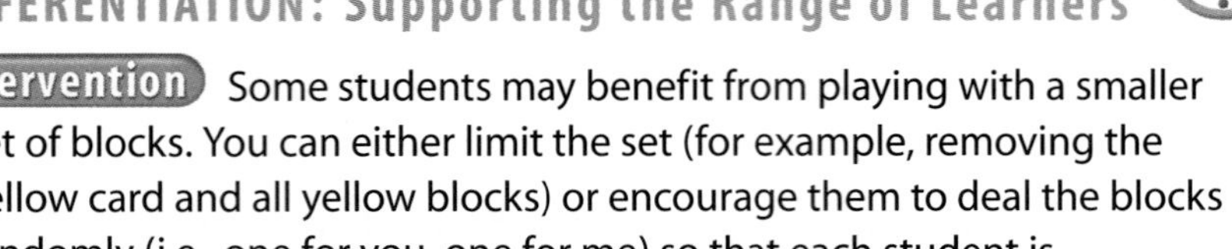

DIFFERENTIATION: Supporting the Range of Learners

Intervention Some students may benefit from playing with a smaller set of blocks. You can either limit the set (for example, removing the yellow card and all yellow blocks) or encourage them to deal the blocks randomly (i.e., one for you, one for me) so that each student is considering only half of the blocks as they play.

5 MIN CLASS

DISCUSSION

4 Checking In

Take this opportunity to discuss any issues that you noticed while observing students at work. The topic might be mathematical in nature, such as a strategy you would like all students to consider (e.g., ways to remember which objects are in the *What's Missing?* set) or a common error or misconception you would like students to discuss (e.g., thinking that only buttons that are exactly the same qualify as matches).

The issue might be logistical (e.g., clarifying the steps of *What's Missing?*) or management-related (e.g., using, sharing, and/or caring for materials, noise level, working productively).

SESSION FOLLOW UP

5 Practice

Practice: For reinforcement of this unit's content, have students complete *Student Activity Book* page 18.

SESSION 1.3

Can You Do What I Do?

Math Focus Points

- Copying a repeating pattern
- Determining what comes next in a repeating pattern
- Counting, creating, and representing quantities
- Comparing how objects are the same and different

Vocabulary

pattern
same
different

Today's Plan		Materials
1 DISCUSSION **Can You Do What I Do?**	5–10 MIN CLASS	
2 MATH WORKSHOP **Missing, Matching, and Counting** 2A Counting Jar 2B *What's Missing?* 2C *Button Match-Up* 2D Sorting Attribute Blocks	15–25 MIN	2A • Counting Jar*; materials for the Counting Jar activity (as you have set it up) 2B • Materials from Session 1.2, p. 29 2C • Materials from Session 1.2, p. 29 2D • Materials from Session 1.2, p. 29
3 DISCUSSION **Same and Different: Buttons**	10 MIN CLASS	• 2 buttons; chart paper with sketches*
4 SESSION FOLLOW-UP **Practice**		• *Student Math Handbook Flip Chart,* pp. 39, 48

*See *Materials to Prepare,* p. 23.

Classroom Routines

Calendar: Days of the Week Use the calendar to review the days of the week, noting which days are school days and which are weekend (or nonschool) days.

DISCUSSION

1 Can You Do What I Do?

5–10 MIN CLASS

Math Focus Points for Discussion

- Copying a repeating pattern
- Determining what comes next in a repeating pattern

Arrange students in a circle so that the whole group can easily see you. Students need space to move around without disturbing one another.

Begin with a two-step pattern of hand gestures such as tapping your shoulders or tapping your head. Choose motions that students can do easily (for example, many kindergarteners cannot snap). Your motions should have a slow and steady beat to them. Ask students to join in and do the actions with you.

Can you do what I do? Can you do it too?

Continue until all students are moving with you. Then ask:

How did you know what to do? How did you know what came next? How would you describe what we were doing to someone else? Many students explain their reasoning and name the **pattern** by describing it.

Students might say:

"Well, first you touched your shoulders, then you touched your head, and then you touched your shoulders again."

"I'd call it 'shoulders, head, shoulders, head.'"

Use this discussion to introduce the word pattern. Each time you use the words [shoulders] and [head], demonstrate that action.

When we did [shoulders, head, shoulders, head] we made a pattern. Our pattern went [shoulders, head, shoulders, head, shoulders, head, shoulders, head]. It's a pattern because it repeats over and over again. ➊ ➋

Math Note

➊ **Kinds of Patterns** There are many kinds of patterns besides repeating patterns that can be described. Although the focus of this unit is on repeating patterns, note that students are likely to come up with other kinds of patterns (for example, ABBCCCDDDD).

Professional Development

➋ **Teacher Note:** Repeating Patterns, p. 147

Do three or four more patterns, as time permits, using gestures such as clapping, standing or sitting, and tapping various parts of your body. Use only two-part patterns. Model the pattern, and continue doing it until all students have joined in. Then, as above, ask:

How did you know what to do? How did you know what came next? . . . How would you describe what we were doing to someone else?

DIFFERENTIATION: Supporting the Range of Learners

ELL Beginning English Language Learners may need some help following the Can You Do What I Do? activities that are repeated throughout this Investigation. To participate fully, students must know the names of different body parts (e.g., *head, shoulders, hands, knees*) and physical actions (e.g., *touch, tap, clap*). During whole-class discussions, try to pair English Language Learners with native English-speaking partners who can help them follow your instructions if necessary.

MATH WORKSHOP

Missing, Matching, and Counting

15–25 MIN

Explain that the following four activities, one of which is the Counting Jar with a new set of materials, are available during Math Workshop. Remind students what each activity entails, what materials are required, and where they are located.

2A Counting Jar

INDIVIDUALS

Students count the objects in the Counting Jar, record the amount counted, and make a set of the same size.

ONGOING ASSESSMENT: Observing Students at Work

Students count a set of objects, create an equivalent set, and record their work.

- **How do students count the objects in the jar?** Do they organize the objects in any way? Do they know the sequence of number names? Do they count each item once and only once? Do they double-check?

- **How do students create an equivalent set?** Do they think, "The Counting Jar had seven, so I need seven [two-color counters]. 1, 2, 3 . . . "? Do they recreate the Counting Jar set, matching items one-to-one? Do they double-check?
- **How do students represent the contents of the jar?** Do they use pictures or symbols? If so, do they draw one for each object or do they draw seven pictures because they counted seven objects? Do they use numbers? How do they figure out how to write a particular number?

2B What's Missing?

For complete details about this activity, see Session 1.2, page 31.

DIFFERENTIATION: Supporting the Range of Learners

Extension Students who are ready for more challenge can rearrange the objects on the tray between each round.

2C Button Match-Up

For complete details about this activity, see Session 1.2, page 32.

DIFFERENTIATION: Supporting the Range of Learners

Extension Challenge students who find matches easily to find more than one match for a given button, or to sort the whole set of buttons according to a given attribute. For example, ask students to explain how one pair matches, and then challenge them to find all the buttons with that attribute.

You said these two buttons are both shiny. Can you find all of the buttons that are shiny?

2D Sorting Attribute Blocks

For complete details about this activity, see Session 1.2, page 33.

DIFFERENTIATION: Supporting the Range of Learners

Extension Students ready for more challenge can select two cards at a time and then find all of the blocks that match those attributes. For example, they might look for blocks that are big and are triangles.

DISCUSSION

Same and Different: Buttons

Math Focus Points for Discussion

- Comparing how objects are the same and different

Show students the large sketches you made of two buttons and pass multiple copies of the buttons themselves around so that students can inspect them.

Here are two of the buttons from our collection. How are they the same?

Students may notice that the size, shape, number of holes, color, material, or other attributes are the same. Write "Same" on the chart paper, and then record the observations students make about how the two buttons are the same.

How are these two buttons different?

Write "Different" on the chart paper, and then record the observations students make about how the two buttons are different.

End by reading aloud a summary of the ways the buttons are the same and different.

SESSION FOLLOW-UP

Practice

Student Math Handbook Flip Chart: Use the *Student Math Handbook Flip Chart* pages 39, 48 to reinforce concepts from today's session. See pages 165–166 in the back of this unit.

SESSION 1.4

Two Kinds of Cube Trains

Math Focus Points

- Copying a repeating pattern
- Determining what comes next in a repeating pattern
- Comparing repeating and non-repeating arrangements

Vocabulary

pattern

Today's Plan			Materials
1 DISCUSSION **Can You Do What I Do?**	5 MIN	CLASS	
2 DISCUSSION **Two Cube Trains**	5–10 MIN	CLASS	• Cube trains*
3 ACTIVITY **Making Cube Trains**	10–20 MIN	INDIVIDUALS	• Connecting cubes
4 DISCUSSION **Sorting Cube Trains**	10 MIN	CLASS	• Cube trains (from Activity 3)
5 SESSION FOLLOW-UP **Practice**			• *Student Math Handbook Flip Chart*, p. 40

*See *Materials to Prepare,* p. 25.

Classroom Routines

Attendance: What if We Start With . . . ? As usual, count around the circle to determine the total number of students present today. Then ask students what they think would happen if the count began with a different student and why. Choose a different student to start, count again, and discuss what happens.

5 MIN CLASS

DISCUSSION
Can You Do What I Do?

Math Focus Points for Discussion

- Copying a repeating pattern
- Determining what comes next in a repeating pattern

As at the beginning of Session 1.3, begin with several rounds of Can You Do What I Do?

I am going to act out another pattern. Watch carefully and see if you can do what I do.

Act out a pattern with two or three different movements. Continue the pattern until all the students are moving with you. Then ask,

How did you know what to do? How did you know what came next? How would you describe what we were doing to someone else?

Act out several patterns, as time permits, including at least one with three movements (e.g., slap your legs, clap, touch your head).

5–10 MIN CLASS

DISCUSSION
Two Cube Trains

Math Focus Points for Discussion

- Comparing repeating and non-repeating arrangements

Over the next few weeks we are going to look very closely at how different sets of objects are arranged.

Hold up the cube train you prepared with eight assorted cubes.

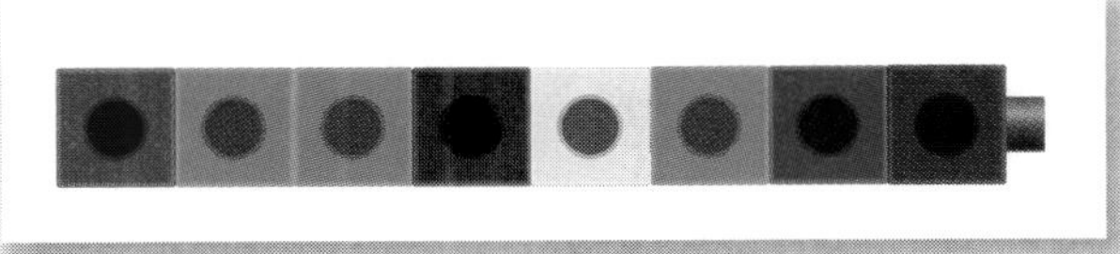

What do you notice about this cube train?

Some students will comment on what it looks like (e.g., a rainbow or train) or talk about color. Others will notice the intricate way the cubes connect. Still others will count the number of cubes used.

Gather as many responses as possible. Then, show students the second train of cubes with colors arranged in an AB pattern.①

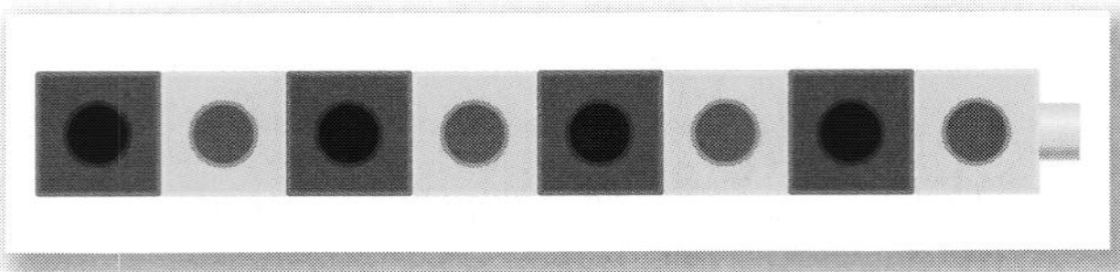

Here's another cube train. What can you tell me about this one?

Again, listen to see how students describe this arrangement. Although many Kindergarten students can recognize and describe the attributes of a pattern, they may not yet know or use the term "pattern." Rather than telling students whether the cube train is (or is not) a pattern, gather as many responses as possible.

Finally, ask students to compare the two sets of cubes.

We looked carefully at this cube train and then at this cube train. What if I put them next to each other? What do you notice? What is the same about them? What is different?②

Explain that students will have the chance to make their own cube trains.

Just like mine, each train you make should have eight cubes. They can look like one of these trains that we have been talking about, or they can look different. At the end of our work time, you will choose one of your cube trains to share with the group.

ACTIVITY 3 Making Cube Trains

10–20 MIN INDIVIDUALS

Students make trains with eight cubes. They choose their favorite to share.

ONGOING ASSESSMENT: Observing Students at Work

Students make arrangements of eight cubes.

- **Are students able to make a train with exactly eight cubes?**
- **Do students make repeating or non-repeating arrangements?** What language do they use to describe them? To compare them to other trains?

Circulate as students work and ask them to describe their arrangements. You might ask them to compare their train to the two trains just discussed.

Math Note

① **Naming Patterns** One common convention uses letters to name patterns. For example, a pattern that alternates blue and green (or two other colored) cubes is called an AB pattern, and one that alternates three different colors is an ABC pattern. Wait until students have discussed the word *pattern* and have had opportunities to make, extend, and discuss a variety of patterns, before introducing the AB/ABC convention and using it with students. Good opportunities to do so are built into the discussions in Session 1.4, p. 43, and Session 1.5, p. 48.

Professional Development

② **Dialogue Box:** Two Arrangements of Color, p. 155

DIFFERENTIATION: Supporting the Range of Learners

Intervention Some students have difficulty counting accurately when cubes are snapped together in a train. Suggest that these students separate the cubes in their train to count them. They may find it easier to count the cubes and then snap them together. You can also provide a train of eight cubes that students can use as a reference. At the end of this work time, remind students to choose one cube train they'd like to share with the class. They should break apart the rest of their trains and return the cubes to the bins.

DISCUSSION

Sorting Cube Trains

10 MIN CLASS

Math Focus Points for Discussion

- Comparing repeating and non-repeating arrangements
- Determining what comes next in a repeating pattern

Gather students together so that they can see one another's cube trains.

Take a look at the different cube trains that people made. What do you notice?

After a few students have shared observations, suggest a way of grouping the trains.

Let's organize your trains into two piles. I noticed that some students used two colors and some students used lots of colors. If you used two colors to make your train, put it in this pile. If you made a train with lots of colors, put it in this pile.③

If students are unsure where to place their work, make suggestions so that this part of the activity moves along fairly quickly. If there are questionable trains, place them in a third pile. Organize the piles so that everyone can see them.

Look very carefully at our groups. What do you notice?

As you gather responses, ask students to explain their reasoning. Listen for evidence that suggests that they have identified the predictable nature of a pattern.④

Teaching Note

③ **Sorting Cube Trains** Although many of the two-color trains will be patterns, some may not be. Some of the trains that use more than two colors may be patterns. This is fine, as this type is based purely on the number of colors used. The use of this type lays the groundwork for the discussion of patterns (and non-patterns), and the introduction of the term *pattern,* which follows.

Professional Development

④ **Dialogue Box:** Sharing Our Cube Trains, p. 157

Teaching Note

❺ **Have Cubes Available** Some teachers put cubes out and ask students to hold up the color cube they think comes next. This strategy encourages more students to be involved and enables the teacher to see the responses of individual students in a group discussion.

Professional Development

❻ **Dialogue Box:** What Might Come Next?, p. 159

❼ **Teacher Note:** Repeating Patterns, p. 147

Next, choose an AB pattern train from the two-color group and a train that is not a pattern from the multicolored group. Ask the following questions about each.

If I were to add another cube to the end of this train, what color would go here? Why do you think that?❺

Encourage students to explain their thinking, and to compare the two trains.

Why do you think [red] would come next? Are you sure? Why or why not? Why is it easy to tell what comes next in this one, but not so easy in this one?❻

If, by the end of this discussion, no one has labeled the two-color train a pattern, introduce the word yourself.

Some of you were pretty sure you could tell what would come next in this train. That's because the cubes in this train make a pattern. They go [red, yellow, red, yellow, red, yellow]. In this kind of pattern, something repeats over and over again. The cubes in this other train do not make a pattern.❼

Save some of students' cube trains for use in Session 1.5. Save a few that are patterns, including any non-AB patterns they created, and a few that are not.

SESSION FOLLOW-UP

Practice

Student Math Handbook Flip Chart: Use the *Student Math Handbook Flip Chart* page 40 to reinforce concepts from today's session. See pages 165–166 in the back of this unit.

SESSION 1.5

Cube Train Patterns

Math Focus Points

- Copying and constructing repeating patterns
- Determining what comes next in a repeating pattern
- Comparing repeating patterns

Vocabulary

describe

Today's Plan		Materials
1 DISCUSSION **Can You Do What I Do?**	5 MIN CLASS	
2 ACTIVITY **Introducing Cube Train Patterns**	5 MIN CLASS	• Cube train patterns*
3 MATH WORKSHOP **Patterns, Counting, and Matching** 3A Cube Train Patterns 3B Counting Jar 3C *What's Missing?* 3D *Button Match-Up* 3E Sorting Attribute Blocks	10–25 MIN	3A • M3* ☑ • Connecting cubes 3B • Materials from Session 1.3, p. 35 3C • Materials from Session 1.2, p. 29 3D • Materials from Session 1.2, p. 29 3E • Materials from Session 1.2, p. 29
4 DISCUSSION **Comparing Cube Train Patterns**	10 MIN CLASS	• Students' cube train patterns (from Math Workshop and Session 1.4)
5 SESSION FOLLOW-UP **Practice**		• *Student Math Handbook Flip Chart,* p. 40

*See *Materials to Prepare,* p. 25.

Classroom Routines

Today's Question: Would you rather eat peas or carrots? **On chart paper, create a vertical two-column table titled "Would you rather eat peas or carrots?" with the label "Peas" written at the bottom of one column and "Carrots" written at the bottom of the other column. Students respond by writing their names above the appropriate heading. Count the responses as a class, and discuss what the results of the survey tell you.**

DISCUSSION

Can You Do What I Do?

Math Focus Points for Discussion

- Copying repeating patterns
- Determining what comes next in a repeating pattern

As you have been doing, begin this session with several rounds of Can You Do What I Do?

I am going to make another pattern. Watch carefully and see whether you can do what I do.

Act out a pattern and continue until all the students are moving with you. Then, ask:

How did you know what to do? How did you know what came next? . . . How would you describe what we were doing to someone else?

Act out several patterns as time permits, including at least one that has the same movement twice in a row (e.g., stamp, stamp, clap, stamp, stamp, clap).

ACTIVITY

Introducing Cube Train Patterns

Show students the cube trains you chose from the ones they made yesterday. Hold up one that is not a pattern.

What do you think will come next in this train? It is hard to figure out what might come next because it is not a pattern.

Then, hold up a train with cubes arranged in an AB pattern.

What do you think comes next in this train? Most people said [yellow] will come next. It was easier to tell because this is a pattern. It goes [yellow, red, yellow, red, yellow, red]. [Yellow, red] repeats over and over.

Ask students to determine what will come next on a few more trains. If students made any trains that show patterns other than AB, discuss a few of those. Then, put all of the trains that are patterns together.

All of these cube trains are patterns. They all have something that repeats over and over. During Math Workshop today, we will do one activity that involves making patterns with cubes. You can make a train that is like one of these or you can make a different pattern. Your cube trains need to be eight, nine, or ten cubes long.

MATH WORKSHOP

Patterns, Counting, and Matching

10–25 MIN

Explain that five activities are available during Math Workshop. Remind students what each activity entails, what materials are required, and where they are located. This is the last day *What's Missing?*, *Button Match-Up,* and Sorting Attribute Blocks will be available.

3A Cube Train Patterns

INDIVIDUALS

Students make patterns with 8, 9, or 10 cubes. ➊ ➋

ONGOING ASSESSMENT: Observing Students at Work

Students construct repeating patterns.

- **Can students make a pattern?** What kinds of patterns do they make? Do any make patterns other than AB?
- **Are students able to make a train with 8, 9, or 10 cubes?**

As you observe, save or note the variety of trains that students create, being sure to include any that show non-ABAB patterns, to inform the discussion at the end of this session.

DIFFERENTIATION: Supporting the Range of Learners

Intervention If students make trains that are not patterns, remind them what you mean by pattern—something that repeats over and over. Talk through an 8-cube example with them. Students who still struggle to make a pattern may benefit from extending a 4-cube train or copying an 8-cube pattern.

Teaching Note

➊ **Assessing Patterns** By the end of this unit, students are expected to be able to copy, construct, and extend simple repeating patterns (Benchmark 1). Use Assessment Checklist: Repeating Patterns (M3) to keep track of your observations about students' patterns over the course of this unit.

Professional Development

➋ **Teacher Notes:** Repeating Patterns, p. 147, and Assessment: Repeating Patterns, p. 149

Assessment Checklist: Repeating Patterns

Student	Kinds of patterns students construct	Copy/extend a pattern type	Notes

© Pearson Education K

Session 1.5 Unit 3 M3

▲ Resource Masters, M3

Math Note

❸ **Generalizing** Throughout this unit, students make, identify, and extend patterns. Although all students are expected to be able to do this by the end of this unit, and many will be able to describe how the pattern repeats ("it goes red, blue, red, blue"), most kindergarteners will not yet be able to generalize about and articulate how a green–yellow train is the same as a blue–red one. Introducing "AB pattern" as one way of describing both patterns may help students who are ready to make such generalizations.

3B Counting Jar

INDIVIDUALS

For complete details about this activity, see Session 1.3, page 37.

3C *What's Missing?*

GROUPS PAIRS

For complete details about this activity, see Session 1.2, pages 30–32.

3D *Button Match-Up*

GROUPS PAIRS

For complete details about this activity, see Session 1.2, page 32.

3E Sorting Attribute Blocks

GROUPS PAIRS

For complete details about this activity, see Session 1.2, page 33.

DISCUSSION

4 Comparing Cube Train Patterns

10 MIN CLASS

Math Focus Points for Discussion

- Determining what comes next in a repeating pattern
- Comparing repeating patterns

Show students some cube trains based on your observations of students' work.

Here are some of the cube trains I saw some students make. They are all patterns.

Hold up two AB trains that are made with eight cubes and use different colors.

What do you notice? How are they the same? How are they different?

Students notice a range of similarities: both trains have eight cubes, use two colors, and the colors alternate. Most students say they are different because they use different colors.❸

Now hold up another one of the AB pattern trains.

Suppose you wanted someone to build a pattern just like this one. How would you describe it?

Some students describe cube trains as "like a candy cane" or "it looks like a train." This is fine, but also encourage students to describe each cube in the pattern. If students are not sure what you mean, model this yourself.

I might describe it like this: [red, yellow, red, yellow, red, yellow, red, yellow].④

Ask students to describe another AB train and to determine what comes next.

[Emma] said this pattern is [green, orange, green, orange, green, orange, green, orange]. If the pattern continues in the same way, what do you think will come next?

Some students choose a color for nonmathematical reasons. Others understand that it must be [green] or [orange], and still others are sure it must be [green].

Finally, ask students to describe a non-AB pattern and to determine what comes next.

[Kyle] said this pattern is [yellow, green, green, yellow, green, green, yellow, green, green]. If the pattern continues in the same way, what do you think will come next?

Identifying what comes next in a non-AB pattern may be more difficult for students. Encourage students to explain their thinking and to consider whether the color they chose will continue the pattern.

SESSION FOLLOW-UP
Practice

Student Math Handbook Flip Chart: Use the *Student Math Handbook Flip Chart* page 40 to reinforce concepts from today's session. See pages 165–166 in the back of this unit.

Math Note

④ **Describing Patterns** Asking students to describe their patterns aloud helps cement their understanding of a pattern sequence. Verbalizing what they see gives students clues about what comes next. Describing their pattern in more than one way helps in forming generalizations.

INVESTIGATION 2

Mathematical Emphasis

Repeating Patterns Constructing, describing, and extending repeating patterns

Math Focus Points

- Copying, constructing, comparing, describing, and recording repeating patterns
- Determining what comes next in a repeating pattern
- Distinguishing between patterns and non-patterns

This Investigation also focuses on

- Counting, creating, and representing quantities
- Counting 12 objects

Constructing Patterns

	Student Activity Book	Student Math Handbook Flip Chart	Professional Development: Read Ahead of Time
SESSION 2.1 p. 58 **Making Patterns** Students copy a pattern made with hand and body motions, and then use a variety of materials to construct their own patterns. Class discussion focuses on the Counting Jar.	19		
SESSION 2.2 p. 65 **Patterns on the Pocket Chart** Students learn another of the yearlong Kindergarten Classroom Routines, *Patterns on the Pocket Chart,* which focuses on identifying, describing, and extending patterns. Math Workshop focuses on using a variety of materials to make patterns.		41	• **Dialogue Box:** I Think It's Green, p. 161 • **Part 4: Classroom Routines** in *Implementing Investigations in Kindergarten:* Patterns on the Pocket Chart
SESSION 2.3 p. 70 **Recording Cube Train Patterns** Students discuss ways to record a cube train pattern. Math Workshop focuses on using a variety of materials to make and record patterns.		40, 41	

Classroom Routines See page 18 for an overview.

Today's Question

- Today's Question Chart for Session 2.3 and 2.6. See instructions on pages 70 and 85.

Calendar

- Monthly calendar or class pocket calendar

Attendance

- No materials needed

Patterns on the Pocket Chart

- Pocket Chart(s) or Sentence Pocket Chart
- Pattern blocks
- M15, Arrow Cards for the Pocket Chart Copy and cut apart.
- M5, Question Mark Cards Copy and cut apart.

Materials to Gather	Materials to Prepare
• **Pattern blocks** (1 container per 3-4 students) • **Two-color counters** (20 per student) • **Materials for Cube Train Patterns** See Session 1.5, p. 45. • **Materials for Counting Jar** See Session 1.3, p. 35. • **Two plates**	• **M4, Pattern Paths** Cut and glue as indicated. (optional, as needed for differentiation) • **Repeating patterns** Gather several samples of items with repeating patterns to introduce the homework assignment, *Patterns from Home*. Continue adding examples between now and the unveiling of the Pattern Display in Investigation 3.
• **M4** (as needed; from Session 2.1) • **Square tiles** (6 of each color plus 1 container per 3–4 students) • **Materials for Pattern Block Patterns** See Session 2.1. • **Materials for Two-Color Counter Patterns** See Session 2.1. • **Materials for Cube Train Patterns** See Session 1.5, p. 45.	• **M5, Question Mark Cards** Copy on cardstock and cut apart. • **Pocket 100 Chart** Display the chart where it can easily be seen. • **Cups or bags of square color tiles** Place one of each color in a small cup or bag. (1 per pair)
• **Pattern blocks** (6 of each) • **Cubes** (6 of each of 2 colors) • **Crayons and/or other coloring materials that match the colors of the cubes** • **Folders for storing student work** (1 per student) • **Tape** (as needed) • **Materials for *Patterns on the Pocket Chart*** See Session 2.2. • **Materials for Cube Train Patterns** See Session 1.5, p. 45. • **Materials for Square Tile Patterns** See Session 2.2. • **Materials for Pattern Block Patterns** See Session 2.1. • **Materials for Two-Color Counter Patterns** See Session 2.1.	• **M6, Cube Strips** Make copies and cut apart into individual strips (several per student, plus extras). • **Cups or bags of pattern blocks** Place one of each pattern block shape in a paper cup or bag. (1 cup or bag per pair)

Constructing Patterns, *continued*

	Student Activity Book	Student Math Handbook Flip Chart	Professional Development: Read Ahead of Time
SESSION 2.4 p. 75 **Pattern Block Snakes** Students use paper pattern block shapes to make and record pattern "snakes."		41	
SESSION 2.5 p. 80 **One-Two Patterns** Students are introduced to patterns that are based on the quantity in each element. Math Workshop continues to focus on using a variety of materials to make and record patterns.			
SESSION 2.6 p. 85 **What Comes Next?** In *What Comes Next?* one student makes a pattern and hides the last few objects. The other student copies the visible part of the pattern and then determines what comes next. Math Workshop continues to focus on one-two patterns and building and recording patterns.	21		• **Dialogue Box:** A "Harder" Pattern, p. 163
SESSION 2.7 p. 90 **Is It a Pattern?** Students record patterns made with two-color counters. They continue to make and record their own patterns and to copy and extend others' patterns.		41, 42	

Materials to Gather	Materials to Prepare
• **Materials for *Patterns on the Pocket Chart*** See Session 2.3. • **Pattern blocks** (1 bucket per 4–6 students) • **Glue sticks** (I per pair)	• **M7–M12, Pattern Block Cutouts** Copy pages onto colored paper and cut apart individual shapes. For hexagons, make 25 copies on yellow paper; for trapezoids, make 10 copies on red paper; for blue rhombuses, make 10 copies on blue paper; for triangles, make 5 copies on green paper; for squares, make 10 copies on orange paper; and for tan rhombuses, make 5 copies on tan paper. • **Paper strips** Cut 12″ x 18″ white paper into 2″ x 10″ strips. Make strips that are 2″ x 20″. (2 per student plus extras)
• **Square tiles** (1 container per 3–4 students) • **Materials for Pattern Block Snakes** See Session 2.4. • **Materials for Recording Cube Train Patterns** See Session 2.3.	• **M13, Family Letter** Make copies. (1 per student)
• **M4, Pattern Paths** (optional) See Session 2.1. • **Teddy bear or other counters** (1 bin per pair) • **Small opaque cups** (4–5 per pair) • **Materials for One-Two Patterns** See Session 2.5. • **Materials for Pattern Block Snakes** See Session 2.4. • **Materials for Recording Cube Train Patterns** See Session 2.3.	
• **Two-color counters (12)** • **Red and yellow crayons** • **Tape** (optional) • **Materials for Two-Color Counter Patterns** See Session 2.1. • **Materials for *What Comes Next?*** See Session 2.6. • **Materials for One-Two Patterns** See Session 2.5. • **Materials for Pattern Block Snakes** See Session 2.4. • **Materials for Recording Cube Train Patterns** See Session 2.3.	• **M14, Two-Color Counter Strips** Make copies and cut apart into individual strips. (3 per student, plus extras) • **Paper strips and colored paper squares** Cut paper that matches the colors of the square tiles into one-inch squares. Cut white paper into 2″ strips. Make strips that are 2″ x 20″. (as needed for Differentiation) • **Non-pattern snake** Use two colors to make a non-pattern snake (e.g., triangle, triangle, square, triangle, square, square, square, triangle).

Constructing Patterns, *continued*

	Student Activity Book	Student Math Handbook Flip Chart	Professional Development: Read Ahead of Time
SESSION 2.8 p. 95			
Arrow Patterns Students make and act out Arrow Patterns that use directionality as an attribute. Math Workshop continues to focus on making and recording their own patterns, and copying and extending others' patterns.		41, 42	
SESSION 2.9 p. 99			
Add On Students learn, play, and discuss *Add On,* a game that involves rolling a dot cube, taking that many cubes, and using them to build a 12-cube 2-color pattern.		40, 41	
SESSION 2.10 p. 103			
Sharing Patterns Students are introduced to *Add On* with different materials. Math Workshop focuses on constructing, extending, and recording patterns. Class discussion focuses on looking at students' work.		41, 42	

Materials to Gather	Materials to Prepare
• **Materials for Patterns on the Pocket Chart** See Session 2.2. • **Materials for *What Comes Next?*** See Session 2.6. • **Materials for One-Two Patterns** See Session 2.5. • **Materials for Recording Two-Color Counter Patterns** See Session 2.7.	• **M15, Arrow Cards for the Pocket Chart** Make 1 copy on cardstock and cut the sheet into cards. • **M16, Arrow Cards** Make 6 copies. Cut each sheet into cards.
• **Connecting cubes** (1 bin per 4–6 students) • **Stick-on dots** (as needed)	• **1-to-2 dot cubes** Label 3 sides of a cube with 1 dot and the other 3 sides with 2 dots. (1 per pair)
• **1-to-2 dot cube** (1) • **Connecting cubes** (1 bin) • **Pattern blocks** (1 container for 4–6 students) • **Two-color counters** (about 20 per pair) • **Glue** (optional) • **Folders of student work** (1 per student) • **Materials for *Add On*** See Session 2.9. • **Materials for Arrow Patterns** See Session 2.8. • **Materials for Recording Two-Color Counter Patterns** See Session 2.7. • **Materials for *What Comes Next?*** See Session 2.6. • **Materials for One-Two Patterns** See Session 2.5. • **Students' recorded patterns**	

Making Patterns

Math Focus Points

- Copying and constructing repeating patterns
- Determining what comes next in a repeating pattern
- Counting, creating, and representing quantities

Today's Plan			Materials
1 DISCUSSION **Can You Do What I Do?**	5 MIN	CLASS	
2 ACTIVITY **Introducing Making Patterns**	5 MIN	CLASS	• Pattern blocks; two-color counters
3 MATH WORKSHOP **Patterns with Pattern Blocks, Counters, and Cubes** 3A Pattern Block Patterns 3B Two-Color Counter Patterns 3C Cube Train Patterns 3D Counting Jar	10–25 MIN		3A • M4 (optional)* • Pattern blocks 3B • M4 (optional)* • Two-color counters 3C • Materials from Session 1.5, p. 45 3D • Materials from Session 1.3, p. 35
4 DISCUSSION **Counting Jar**	10 MIN	CLASS	• Materials from Session 1.3, p. 35 • Two-color counters, 2 plates
5 SESSION FOLLOW-UP **Homework**			• *Student Activity Book,* p. 19 • Examples of repeating patterns*

*See *Materials to Prepare,* p. 53.

Classroom Routines

Calendar: What's Missing? **Remove two dates on the monthly calendar. Challenge students to tell you which cards are missing and how they know.**

DISCUSSION

Can You Do What I Do?

5 MIN CLASS

Math Focus Points for Discussion

- Copying repeating patterns
- Determining what comes next in a repeating pattern

As you have been doing, begin this session with several rounds of Can You Do What I Do?

I am going to make another pattern. Watch carefully and see whether you can do what I do.

Act out a pattern and continue until all the students are moving with you. Then, ask:

How did you know what to do? How did you know what came next? . . . How would you describe what we were doing to someone else?

Do several patterns, as time permits, including at least one that has the same movement twice in a row (e.g., clap, clap, stamp, clap, clap, stamp).❶

ACTIVITY

Introducing Making Patterns

5 MIN CLASS

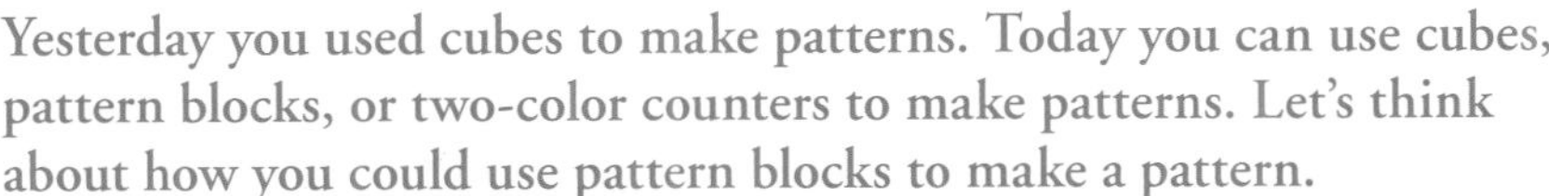

Yesterday you used cubes to make patterns. Today you can use cubes, pattern blocks, or two-color counters to make patterns. Let's think about how you could use pattern blocks to make a pattern.

Make an AB pattern using two different types of pattern blocks. Put out six blocks.

I made a pattern using the pattern blocks. My pattern is [green triangle, orange square, green triangle, orange square, green triangle, orange square]. What do you think will be the next block in my pattern?❷

Teaching Note

❶ **Continuing Can You Do What I Do?** Some teachers use this game as a routine during transition times or to get students' attention. It is important to periodically ask students to describe the pattern and to discuss how they know what comes next. Students can also play in pairs or small groups.

Math Note

❷ **Vocabulary** Use both color and shape words as you refer to the pattern blocks, so students who are not yet familiar with terms like *triangle* and *square* can understand your pattern, and so they hear such terms used properly, in context. The geometry unit, *Make a Shape, Build a Block*, will provide experiences that focus on shapes, their names, and attributes.

Math Note

3 **Non-cube Patterns** In Investigation 1, students were specifically asked to make pattern trains—to link together 8, 9, or 10 cubes in a patterned arrangement. With the introduction of pattern blocks and two-color counters, you may see a wider range of patterns (and non-patterns).

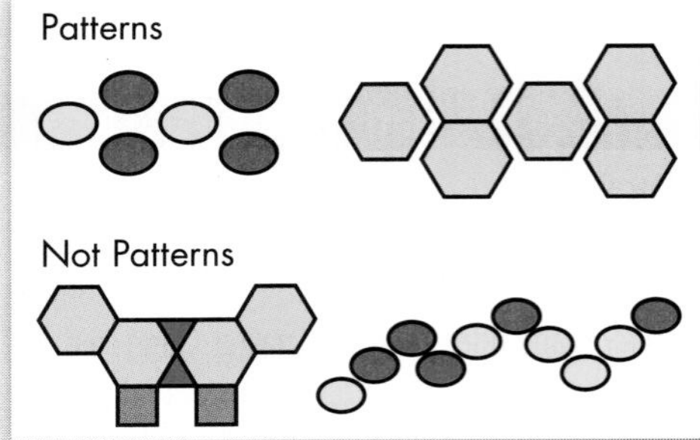

Ask several students to add a block to your pattern. Each time, ask them to explain why they think the block they chose comes next in your pattern.

Students make pattern block patterns.

When you work with the pattern blocks you might make a pattern like mine or a different pattern.

Also introduce the two-color counters.

Think for a minute about a pattern you could make with the two-color counters.

Ask several students to describe a pattern they might make with the two-color counters.3

MATH WORKSHOP

10–25 MIN

3 Patterns with Pattern Blocks, Counters, and Cubes

Explain that the following four activities are available during Math Workshop. Remind students what each activity entails, what materials are required, and where they are located.

Ask any students who have not yet visited the Counting Jar to do so today, as the discussion at the end of this session will focus on that activity.

3A Pattern Block Patterns

INDIVIDUALS

Students make patterns from pattern blocks.

ONGOING ASSESSMENT: Observing Students at Work

Students make repeating patterns.

- **Are students able to make a pattern?** What types of patterns do they make? Do any make non-AB patterns? 4
- **What language do students use to describe their patterns?** Do they focus on the color of the pattern blocks? The name or orientation of the shape? The number in each part? The total number?

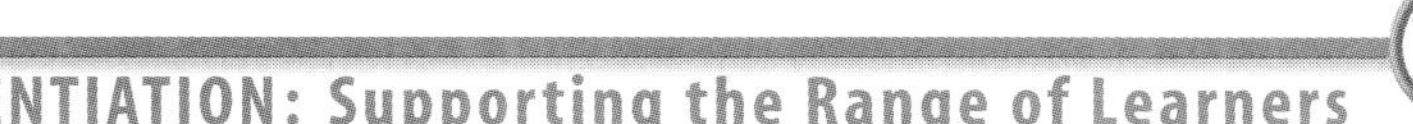

DIFFERENTIATION: Supporting the Range of Learners

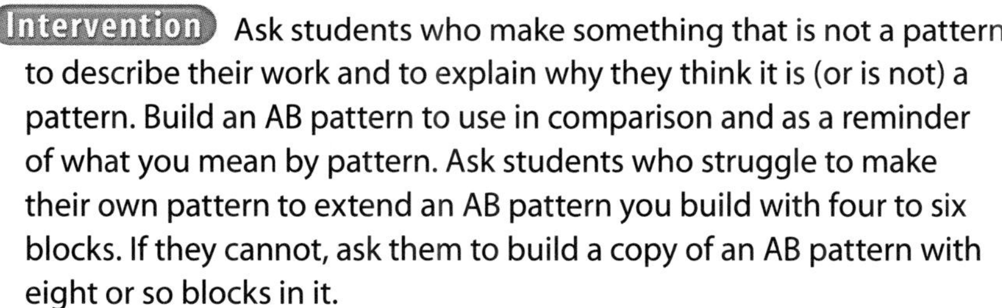

Intervention Ask students who make something that is not a pattern to describe their work and to explain why they think it is (or is not) a pattern. Build an AB pattern to use in comparison and as a reminder of what you mean by pattern. Ask students who struggle to make their own pattern to extend an AB pattern you build with four to six blocks. If they cannot, ask them to build a copy of an AB pattern with eight or so blocks in it.

Intervention Some students may benefit from using a Pattern Path (M4) to organize their work, placing one object in each square.

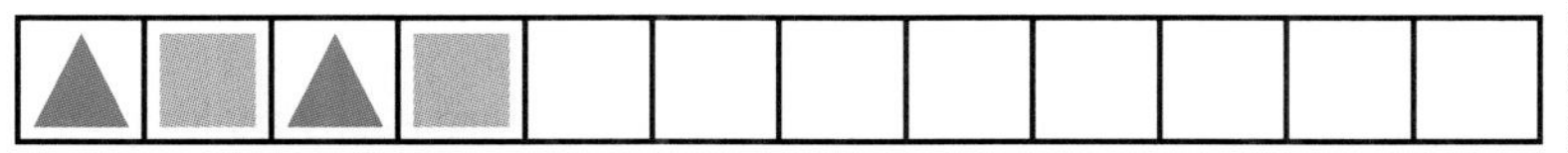

3B Two-Color Counter Patterns

INDIVIDUALS

Students make patterns with two-color counters.

Math Note

4 **What Does Pattern Mean?** The goal of this unit is to both expand and refine students' notions of what constitutes a pattern. Some students think that *pattern* applies to arrangements, designs, or even anything made with pattern blocks. Some teachers help students develop meaning for the term by using terms like *arrangement* or *design* for constructions that do not have a discernible repetition or regularity, reserving *pattern* for work that clearly shows repetition or regularity.

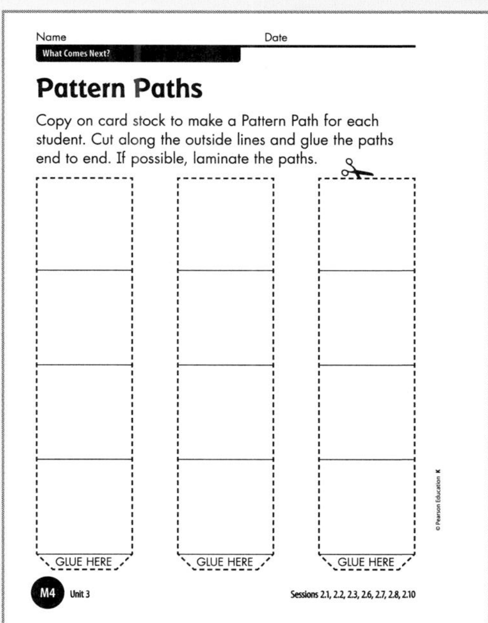

Name Date

What Comes Next?

Pattern Paths

Copy on card stock to make a Pattern Path for each student. Cut along the outside lines and glue the paths end to end. If possible, laminate the paths.

GLUE HERE GLUE HERE GLUE HERE

M4 Unit 3 Sessions 2.1, 2.2, 2.3, 2.6, 2.7, 2.8, 2.10

▲ Resource Masters, M4

ONGOING ASSESSMENT: Observing Students at Work

Students make repeating patterns.

- **Are students able to make a pattern?** What types of patterns do they make? Do any make non-AB patterns?
- **What language do students use to describe their patterns?** Do they focus on the color of the chips? Their placement in relation to other chips? The number in each part? The total number?

DIFFERENTIATION: Supporting the Range of Learners

Intervention Ask students who make something that is not a pattern to describe their work and to explain why they think it is (or is not) a pattern. Build an AB pattern to use in comparison and as a reminder of what you mean by pattern. Ask students who struggle to make their own pattern to extend an AB pattern you build with 4 to 6 chips. If they cannot, ask them to build a copy of an AB pattern with eight or so chips in it.

Intervention Some students may benefit from using a Pattern Path (M4) to organize their work, placing one object in each square.

3C Cube Train Patterns

For complete details about this activity, see Session 1.5, page 46.

DIFFERENTIATION: Supporting the Range of Learners

Extension Challenge students who are easily making AB patterns to construct other kinds of patterns.

3D Counting Jar

For complete details about this activity, see Session 1.3, page 37.

DISCUSSION

Counting Jar

Math Focus Points for Discussion

- Counting, creating, and representing quantities

Place the Counting Jar poster, with students' representations on it, so that all the students can see it. (Or, if students record in individual Counting Jar booklets, ask them to bring them to the discussion, open to that page.)

Ask the students how many cubes they found in the Counting Jar. Have several students count the cubes, and then count them together to check.

Then, show students two collections of 7 two-color counters, each on its own plate. On one, show five yellow and two red counters; on the other show six red and one yellow.

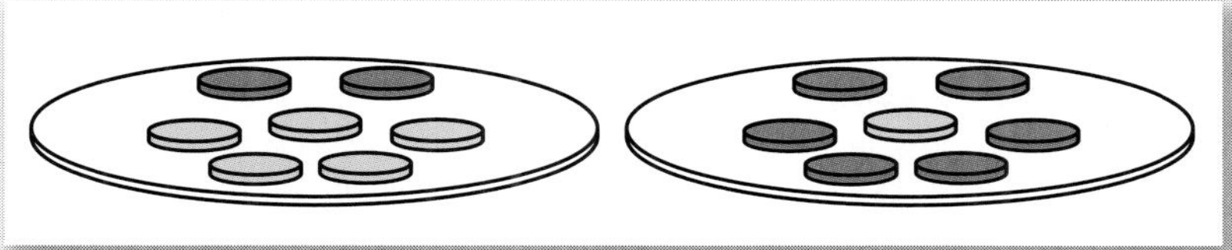

Ask students whether each collection shows seven. Although students may agree that both plates show a group of seven, they may have a harder time seeing how the collections are the same (both have seven) when they look so different (five and two vs. one and six). Take this opportunity to probe students' developing understanding of the equivalence of two different sets.

[Kiyo] and [Mitchell] both counted the counters on this plate and got seven. [Jack] and [Tammy] both counted the counters on this plate, and they got seven. If both plates have seven, why do they look so different? I see a lot of reds on this plate, and the other plate doesn't have very many reds.

Teaching Note

❺ **Who Did It This Way?** Asking students to raise their hands if they used a particular method of recording allows many students to participate without using the time it takes to have each student share.

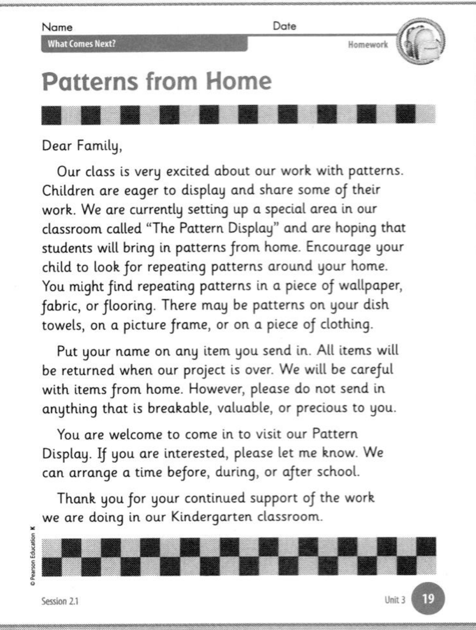

Name Date

What Comes Next? Homework

Patterns from Home

Dear Family,

Our class is very excited about our work with patterns. Children are eager to display and share some of their work. We are currently setting up a special area in our classroom called "The Pattern Display" and are hoping that students will bring in patterns from home. Encourage your child to look for repeating patterns around your home. You might find repeating patterns in a piece of wallpaper, fabric, or flooring. There may be patterns on your dish towels, on a picture frame, or on a piece of clothing.

Put your name on any item you send in. All items will be returned when our project is over. We will be careful with items from home. However, please do not send in anything that is breakable, valuable, or precious to you.

You are welcome to come in to visit our Pattern Display. If you are interested, please let me know. We can arrange a time before, during, or after school.

Thank you for your continued support of the work we are doing in our Kindergarten classroom.

Session 2.1 Unit 3 19

▲ Student Activity Book, p. 19

Finally, discuss the different ways students used to represent what was in the jar.

Take a minute to look at the different ways kids showed how many cubes were in the Counting Jar. What do you notice?

In order to acknowledge all students' work, summarize the recording method, and ask children to raise their hands if they used the one you describe.

I noticed that some people drew squares to show that there were seven cubes in the jar. Raise your hand if you drew squares, or pictures of the cubes. [Point out these representations for students.] . . . Other people used lines to show how many. Who used lines? . . . Some other people used numbers. How many of you wrote numbers? . . . Some people used pictures and numbers. Who drew pictures and wrote numbers? . . . These are all good ways of showing the number of objects in the Counting Jar.❺

5 SESSION FOLLOW-UP
Homework

Homework: Send home with each student a copy of *Student Activity Book* page 19, which explains the assignment to families. Explain that, over the next few weeks, the class will be making a pattern collection. Students will contribute patterns, or items that have a pattern, to make a display. Show students a sample item or two to illustrate what you mean. Then ask students to point out the pattern in your example(s).

SESSION 2.2

Patterns on the Pocket Chart

Math Focus Points

- Describing repeating patterns
- Determining what comes next in a repeating pattern
- Constructing repeating patterns

Vocabulary

pattern

Today's Plan		Materials
1 ACTIVITY **Introducing *Patterns on the Pocket Chart***	10 MIN CLASS	• M5* • Pocket 100 Chart*; square tiles; cups or bags of square color tiles*
2 MATH WORKSHOP **Patterns with Tiles, Pattern Blocks, Counters, and Cubes** 2A Square Tile Patterns 2B Pattern Block Patterns 2C Two-Color Counter Patterns 2D Cube Train Patterns	15–30 MIN	2A • M4 (optional) • Square tiles 2B • Materials from Session 2.1, p. 58 2C • Materials from Session 2.1, p. 58 2D • Materials from Session 1.5, p. 45
3 DISCUSSION **Checking In**	5 MIN CLASS	
4 SESSION FOLLOW-UP **Practice**		• *Student Math Handbook Flip Chart,* p. 41

*See *Materials to Prepare,* p. 53.

Classroom Routines

Attendance: Comparing Groups **Count around the circle as usual, then count the number of boys and the number of girls in class today. Ask students whether there are more boys or girls. Have the boys make a line and the girls make a line opposite them. Count the number of students in each line and again ask whether there are more boys or girls. Challenge students to figure out how many more and discuss their strategies.**

Teaching Notes

➊ **The *Pattern* Routine** This routine, and the variations that are suggested over the course of this unit and year *Kindergarten* provide regular practice with identifying, describing, and extending patterns. For more information, see **Part 4: Classroom Routines** in *Implementing Investigations in Kindergarten* Patterns on the Pocket Chart.

➋ **Kinds of Pocket Charts** This activity uses a pocket 100 chart, which is part of the Kindergarten materials kit. Some teachers find that using two pocket charts side-by-side, or a sentence pocket chart, enables students to look at and extend longer patterns without having the pattern "wrap around" to the next row. If you present longer patterns on one chart, you will have to help students understand that, when the row ends, the pattern continues on the second line.

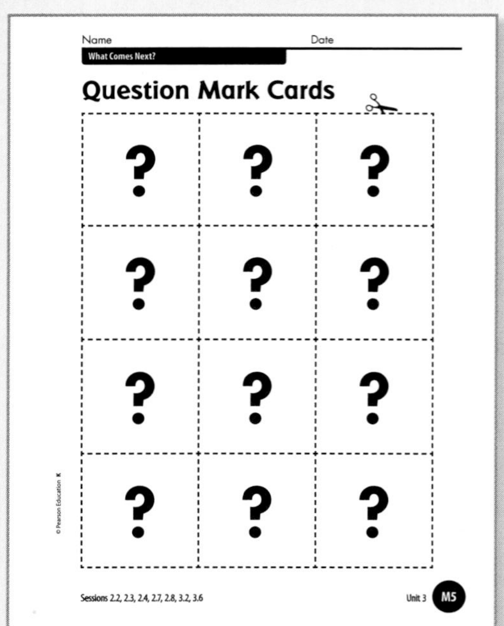
Name Date
What Comes Next?

Question Mark Cards

?	?	?
?	?	?
?	?	?
?	?	?

Sessions 2.2, 2.3, 2.4, 2.7, 2.8, 3.2, 3.6 Unit 3 M5

▲ Resource Masters, M5

ACTIVITY

1 Introducing *Patterns on the Pocket Chart*➊

Begin by secretly making a pattern on the pocket chart. In the first row, make an AB pattern with ten green and yellow square color tiles. Cover the last four tiles with Question Mark Cards (M5).➋

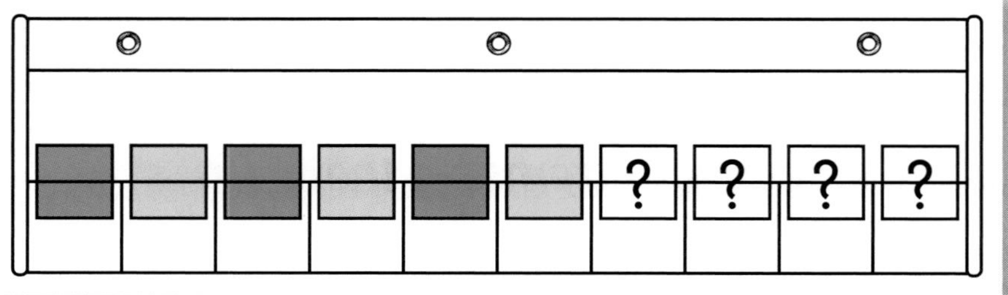

Gather students so they can see the pattern and give each pair a cup of color tiles.

I have started a pattern in this pocket chart. What do you notice about this pattern?

Some students comment on the colors in the pattern or the fact that the pattern is made of tiles. Others note that there are two colors or point out the question marks.

[Rebecca] asked about these cards "with squiggly lines." Those are question marks. Each time you see a Question Mark Card, the question is: "What color do you think is hidden under the card?"

Ask students to look again at the color tiles that are showing.

[Cindy] said the pattern goes green, yellow, green, yellow, green, yellow. Let's describe the pattern together.

Point to each tile as the whole class says the color. Stop were the tiles stop.

Green, yellow, green, yellow, green, yellow. . . . If the pattern continues in the same way, what comes next? What color tile do you think is under this question mark? Talk to your partner. Then, hold up the color tile you think comes next.

Look around at the color tiles students hold up.

Some people think a yellow tile will come next. Why do you think so? Some people think a green tile will come next. Why do you think so?

Students might say:

"There are only yellow and green, so it has to be yellow or green."

"It has to be green because it goes, green, yellow, green, yellow."❸

Reveal the tile under the card. Follow the same process for each Question Mark Card, until you have revealed all the tiles.

Ask a student to say each color in your pattern, in order. Then ask what would happen if the pattern kept going.

If time permits, secretly make another AB pattern, below your first pattern. Use ten red and blue square color tiles, and cover the last four with Question Mark Cards. Follow the same process with this pattern.

Tell students that today during Math Workshop one of the choices will be to make patterns with square tiles.

MATH WORKSHOP

Patterns with Tiles, Pattern Blocks, Counters, and Cubes

15–30 MIN

Explain that the following four activities are available during Math Workshop. In addition to pattern blocks, two-color counters, and cubes, students can make patterns with square tiles. Remind students what each activity entails, what materials are required, and where they are located.

2A Square Tile Patterns

INDIVIDUALS

Students make patterns with square tiles.

Professional Development

❸ **Dialogue Box:** I Think It's Green, p. 161

ONGOING ASSESSMENT: Observing Students at Work

Students make repeating patterns.

- **Are students able to make a pattern?** What types of patterns do they make? Do any make non-AB patterns?
- **What language do students use to describe their patterns?** Do they focus on the color of the tiles? Their placement in relation to other tiles? The number in each part? The total number?

DIFFERENTIATION: Supporting the Range of Learners

Intervention Ask students who make something that is not a pattern to describe their work and to explain why they think it is (or is not) a pattern. Build an AB pattern to use in comparison and as a reminder of what you mean by pattern. Ask students who struggle to make their own pattern to extend an AB pattern you build with 4 to 6 tiles. If they cannot, ask them to build a copy of an AB pattern with eight or so tiles in it.

Some students may benefit from using a Pattern Path (M4) to organize their work, placing one object in each square.

2B Pattern Block Patterns

INDIVIDUALS

For complete details about this activity, see Session 2.1, page 61.

DIFFERENTIATION: Supporting the Range of Learners

Extension Challenge students who are easily making AB patterns to construct other kinds of patterns.

A student makes an ABC pattern.

2C Two-Color Counter Patterns

INDIVIDUALS

For complete details about this activity, see Session 2.1, page 61.

DIFFERENTIATION: Supporting the Range of Learners

Extension Challenge students who are easily making AB patterns to construct other kinds of patterns.

2D Cube Train Patterns

INDIVIDUALS

For complete details about this activity, see Session 1.5, page 46.

3 DISCUSSION

Checking In

5 MIN CLASS

Take this opportunity to discuss any issues that you noticed while observing students at work. The topic might be mathematical (e.g., how to check to see whether something is a pattern), logistical (e.g., taking apart patterns at the end of a work time), or management related (e.g., what to do if one shape or color runs out) that arose during the session.

Other alternatives include checking in with students about which activities they have been choosing (e.g., "Thumbs up if you worked on cube trains. Thumbs up if you worked on pattern block patterns.") or allowing students to raise a question or make a comment about that day's math class.

4 SESSION FOLLOW-UP

Practice

Student Math Handbook Flip Chart: Use the *Student Math Handbook Flip Chart* page 41 to reinforce concepts from today's session. See pages 165–166 in the back of this unit.

Recording Cube Train Patterns

Math Focus Points

- Describing repeating patterns
- Determining what comes next in a repeating pattern
- Constructing and recording repeating patterns

Today's Plan		Materials
1 DISCUSSION *Patterns on the Pocket Chart*	5 MIN CLASS	• Materials from Session 2.2, p. 65; pattern blocks; cups or bags of pattern blocks*
2 ACTIVITY Introducing Recording Cube Train Patterns	5 MIN CLASS	• M6* • Cubes; crayons that match the colors of the cubes; folders
3 MATH WORKSHOP Constructing and Recording Patterns 3A Recording Cube Train Patterns 3B Square Tile Patterns 3C Pattern Block Patterns 3D Two-Color Counter Patterns	15–30 MIN	3A • Materials from Session 1.5, p. 45; cube strips; coloring materials; folders 3B • Materials from Session 2.2, p. 65 3C • Materials from Session 2.1, p. 58 3D • Materials from Session 2.1, p. 58
4 DISCUSSION Checking In	5 MIN CLASS	
5 SESSION FOLLOW-UP Practice		• *Student Math Handbook Flip Chart,* pp. 40, 41

*See *Materials to Prepare,* p. 53.

Classroom Routines

Today's Question: Have you ever been on an airplane? **On chart paper, create a vertical 2-column table titled "Have you ever been on an airplane?" with the heading "Yes" written at the top of one column and "No" written at the top of the other column. Students respond by writing their names below the appropriate heading. Count the responses as a class and discuss what the results of the survey tell you.**

DISCUSSION

Patterns on the Pocket Chart

5 MIN CLASS

Math Focus Points for Discussion

- Describing repeating patterns
- Determining what comes next in a repeating pattern

Secretly make a pattern on the pocket chart. Make an AB pattern with ten pattern blocks, alternating red trapezoids and green triangles. Cover the last four pattern blocks with Question Mark Cards.

Gather students so they can see the pattern and give each pair a cup of pattern blocks.

I have started a pattern in this pocket chart. What do you notice about this pattern?

Encourage students to share their ideas and to describe the pattern. Then ask students to hold up the pattern block they think will come next and to explain why they think so. Reveal the block, and follow the same process for each Question Mark Card. Ask students what they think the pattern would look like if it continued.

Then, follow the same process for an ABC pattern made from orange squares, yellow hexagons, and blue rhombuses (or diamonds).

ACTIVITY

5 MIN CLASS

Introducing Recording Cube Train Patterns

Make an AB pattern with connecting cubes. Ask students to describe your pattern.

You have been making a lot of interesting patterns, but you haven't been able to save them. Today you are going to be able to record the patterns you make with cubes.

Show students the Cube Strips (M6) you have prepared.

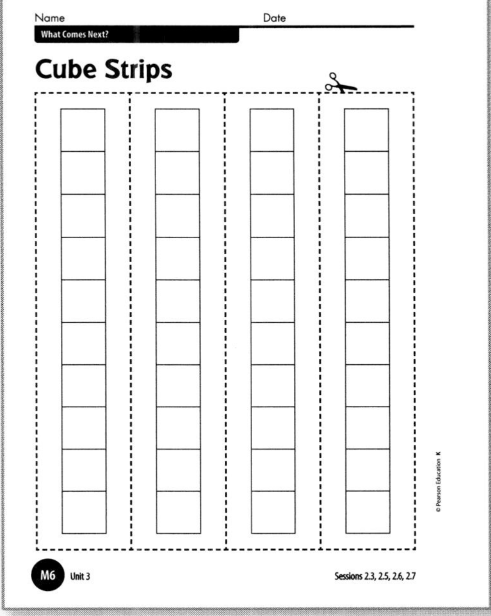

Name Date

What Comes Next?

Cube Strips

© Pearson Education K

M6 Unit 3 Sessions 2.3, 2.5, 2.6, 2.7

▲ Resource Masters, M6

How could we use this cube strip to show my pattern?

Students might say:

"You could color the strip the same as your train."

How could I make sure that I record my pattern correctly?

Students might say:

"You could put the cube train next to this cube strip and copy the colors one by one. If there's a blue here, you color a blue there. If it's red, you color it red."

"You could put a cube on all the squares and then color the square when you take away a cube."

"What if we worked with a partner? One person says red, blue, red, blue. The other person colors red, blue, red, blue."

Discuss students' ideas, and use one to color in your strip.

Explain that if a train is shorter than the strip, students only need to color in as many squares as are in their train. (Students who make trains longer than the strip can tape two strips together.)

Show students the folders you have set aside for storing completed work or work in progress.

3

MATH WORKSHOP

Constructing and Recording Patterns

15–30 MIN

Explain that the following four activities are available during Math Workshop and that today will be the last day students can work with two-color counters until Session 2.7. Remind students what each activity entails, what materials are required, and where they are located.

3A Recording Cube Train Patterns

INDIVIDUALS

Students make and record patterns made with connecting cubes.

ONGOING ASSESSMENT: Observing Students at Work

Students make and record repeating patterns.

- **Are students able to make a pattern with cubes?** What kinds of patterns do they make? Do any make patterns other than AB?
- **How do students record cube train patterns?** Does their cube strip match their cube train? Do they double-check?

DIFFERENTIATION: Supporting the Range of Learners

Intervention Help students who have difficulty accurately recording their patterns to model strategies the class suggested, such as lining up the train with the strip, or breaking the train apart and placing each cube on a square.

If there are students who seem overwhelmed by the recording aspect and they are still working to construct arrangements that are patterns, ask them to continue making patterns. Ask them to record when they seem ready.

3B Square Tile Patterns

INDIVIDUALS

For complete details about this activity, see Session 2.2, page 67.

DIFFERENTIATION: Supporting the Range of Learners

Extension Challenge students who are easily making AB patterns to construct other kinds of patterns.

3C Pattern Block Patterns

INDIVIDUALS

For complete details about this activity, see Session 2.1, page 61.

3D Two-Color Counter Patterns

INDIVIDUALS

For complete details about this activity, see Session 2.1, page 61.

DISCUSSION

Checking In

Take this opportunity to discuss any issues that you noticed while observing students at work. The topic might be mathematical (e.g., strategies for recording a cube train pattern) or relate to a management issue (e.g., returning materials when they are done or using the materials quietly) that arose during the session.

Other alternatives include checking with students about which activities they have been choosing (Who has made a pattern from 2-color counters? Who has made a pattern from pattern blocks?), asking students who recorded a cube train pattern to hold up a piece of work, or allowing students to raise a question or make a comment about that day's math class.

SESSION FOLLOW-UP

5 Practice

Student Math Handbook Flip Chart: Use the *Student Math Handbook Flip Chart* pages 40, 41 to reinforce concepts from today's session. See pages 165–166 in the back of this unit.

SESSION 2.4

Pattern Block Snakes

Math Focus Points

- Describing repeating patterns
- Determining what comes next in a repeating pattern
- Constructing and recording repeating patterns

Today's Plan			Materials
1 DISCUSSION *Patterns on the Pocket Chart*	5 MIN	CLASS	• Materials from Session 2.3, p. 70
2 ACTIVITY Introducing Pattern Block Snakes	5 MIN	CLASS	• M7–M12* • Pattern blocks; paper strips*; glue sticks
3 ACTIVITY Making Pattern Block Snakes	15–30 MIN	INDIVIDUALS	• Materials from Activity 2
4 DISCUSSION Checking In	5 MIN	CLASS	
5 SESSION FOLLOW-UP Practice			• *Student Math Handbook Flip Chart,* p. 41

*See *Materials to Prepare,* p. 55.

Classroom Routines

Calendar: How Many Days . . . ? **Students use the calendar to determine how many days until a class event or holiday that will happen this month. Discuss students' strategies for determining the number of days.**

1 DISCUSSION
Patterns on the Pocket Chart

Math Focus Points for Discussion

- Describing repeating patterns
- Determining what comes next in a repeating pattern

Secretly make a pattern on the Pocket Chart. Make an ABB pattern (red trapezoid, green triangle, green triangle) with ten pattern blocks. Cover the last four pattern blocks with Question Mark Cards.

Gather students so they can see the pattern and give each pair a cup of pattern blocks.

Look carefully at this pattern. What do you notice? It is different from the patterns we have been looking at on the Pocket Chart? Can anyone say how it is different?

Students might say:

"It doesn't go back and forth with two colors."

"There are two triangles next to each other."

[Brad] says there are two green triangles next to each other. It doesn't just alternate red trapezoid, green triangle, red trapezoid, green triangle.

Describe the pattern so far, aloud together.

Let's try to figure out what comes next. Hold up the block that you think will come next.

Encourage students to explain their thinking, then reveal the block. Do the same for each Question Mark Card and then say each shape in the pattern aloud, in order, as a group. Talk briefly about what might come next.

If time permits, follow the same process for an ABB pattern made from green triangles and orange squares.①

Teaching Note

① ***Patterns on the Pocket Chart* as an Ongoing Routine** Once established, this activity is suggested as a Classroom Routine every few days. Much like *Attendance*, it works well as part of a morning routine, outside of math time. Variations are provided over the course of the year, to reflect students' growing understanding of patterns. For more information, see **Part 4: Classroom Routines** in *Implementing Investigations in Kindergarten* Patterns on the Pocket Chart.

DIFFERENTIATION: Supporting the Range of Learners

ELL As the patterns on the pocket chart become more challenging, it may be useful to preview or review key vocabulary with English Language Learners. In order to describe what they notice about this pattern, students must know the names of shapes (*trapezoid, triangle*) as well as colors (*red, green*). You can also help English Language Learners practice sequential vocabulary such as *first, next,* and *after.* Kiyo, what color comes *first* in this pattern? What color comes next? What comes *after* the green triangle? Then encourage English Language Learners to create their own patterns and ask each other similar questions about them.

ACTIVITY

Introducing Pattern Block Snakes

5 MIN CLASS

Today everyone is going to use pattern blocks to make pattern snakes. Your snake should have a pattern that goes from one end to the other.❷

Show students the strips of paper they will use.

You will use 10–12 blocks, or enough to cover a paper strip from one end to the other.

Use pattern blocks to make a pattern on a strip of paper, as an example.

You should make each block touch the block before it. You'll notice that some shapes fit together more easily than others.

Ask students to describe your pattern. Then show students the paper pattern blocks and glue stick.

After you make a pattern, you will use these paper pattern blocks to record your work. How might I use these paper pattern blocks to record my work?

Teaching Note

❷ **Children's Literature** Some teachers introduce this activity with *The Sultan's Snakes* by Lorna Turpin or another book about snakes that includes illustrations of patterns.

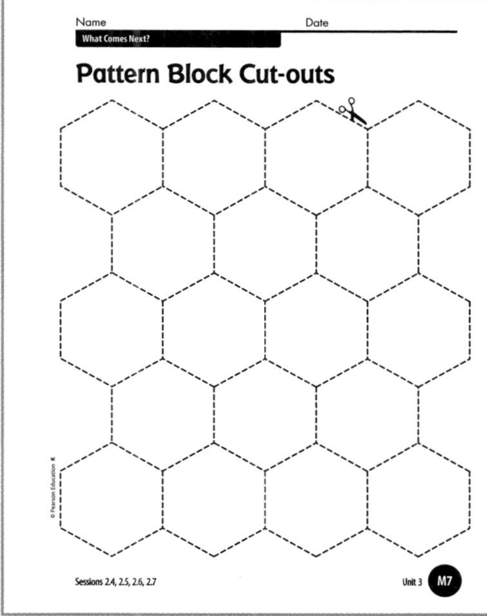

▲ Resource Masters, M7

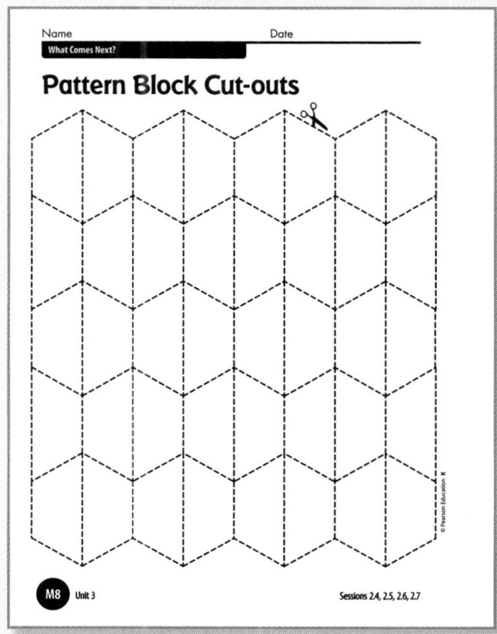

▲ Resource Masters, M8

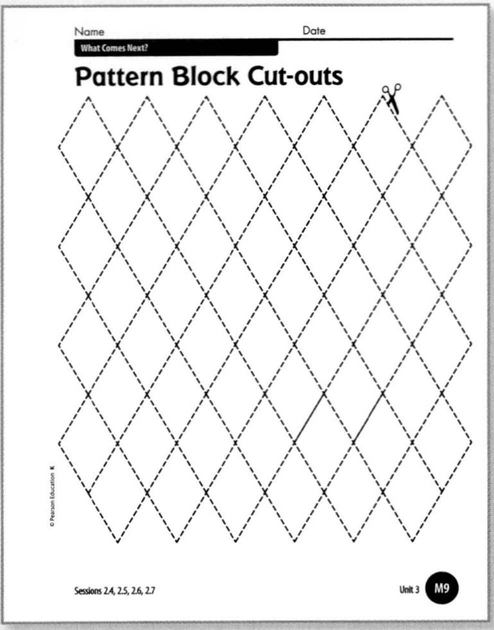

▲ Resource Masters, M9

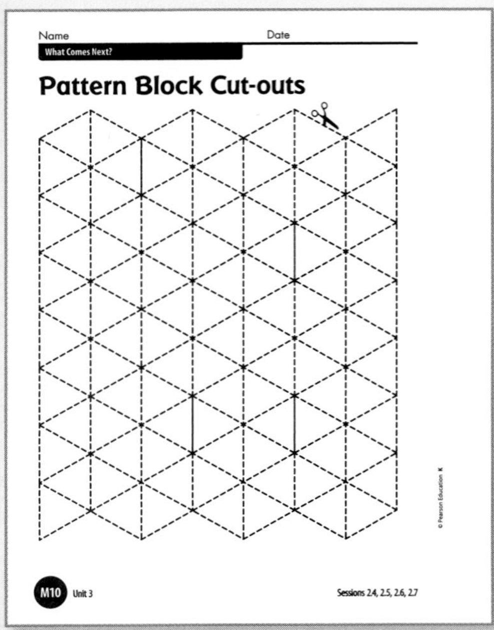

▲ Resource Masters, M10

Some students build on the paper strip and then remove one block at a time and glue down a paper shape in its place. Others line their strip up next to their pattern and create an exact copy, gluing down one shape at a time. Still others internalize their pattern and do not use the blocks as a reference. Discuss each method, and use one to record your sample pattern.

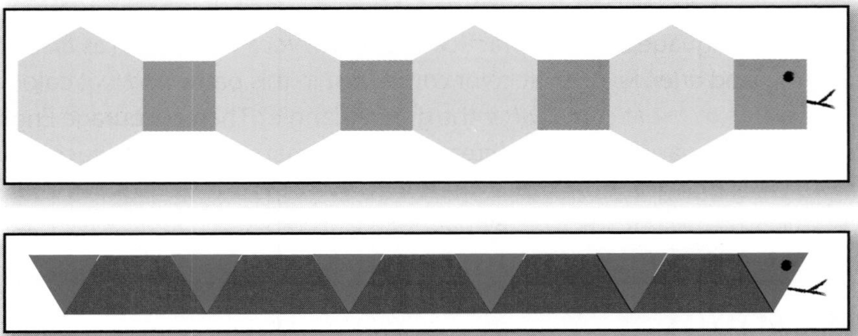

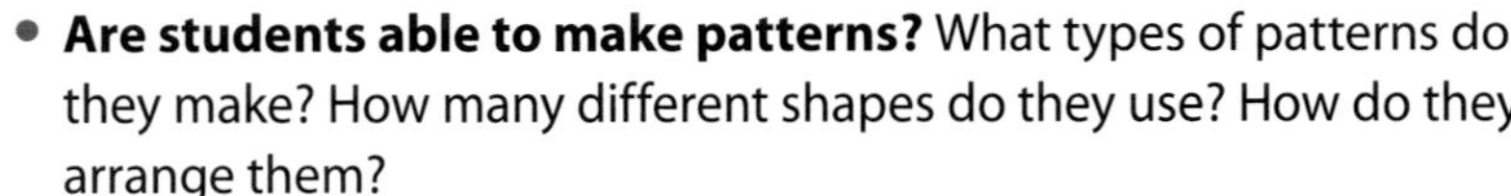

3 ACTIVITY
Making Pattern Block Snakes

15–30 MIN INDIVIDUALS

Students use pattern blocks to make and record pattern block snakes.

ONGOING ASSESSMENT: Observing Students at Work

Students make and record repeating patterns.

- **Are students able to make patterns?** What types of patterns do they make? How many different shapes do they use? How do they arrange them?
- **How do students describe their patterns?** How do they describe the pattern blocks they used? Do they refer to color? Shape? Orientation? Number?
- **How do students record their pattern block snakes?** Can they accurately recreate their pattern on paper? Do they double-check?

DIFFERENTIATION: Supporting the Range of Learners

Intervention Work with students who have difficulty accurately recording their pattern. Model strategies the class suggested, such as lining up the pattern and the paper strip, or building on top of the paper strip and then removing and gluing down one block at a time.

Intervention Some students record a different pattern than the one they made with blocks, or record something that is not a pattern. Encourage students to double-check their work and to compare their paper snake to their pattern block snake. Asking students to describe either pattern (made with blocks or paper shapes) may help them see a block they hadn't intended to place or hear an error they hadn't noticed.

5 MIN CLASS

DISCUSSION

Checking In

End by asking students to hold up one of the pattern block snakes they recorded. Encourage students to consider and comment on the work of their peers. Seeing others' work can trigger a question, spark a new idea, or present a new challenge. For example, a student may become intrigued with finding a way to make a pattern with three different kinds of blocks (e.g., an ABC pattern), or one that uses one kind of block twice (e.g., an AAB pattern).

SESSION FOLLOW-UP

Practice

Student Math Handbook Flip Chart: Use the *Student Math Handbook Flip Chart* page 41 to reinforce concepts from today's session. See pages 165–166 in the back of this unit.

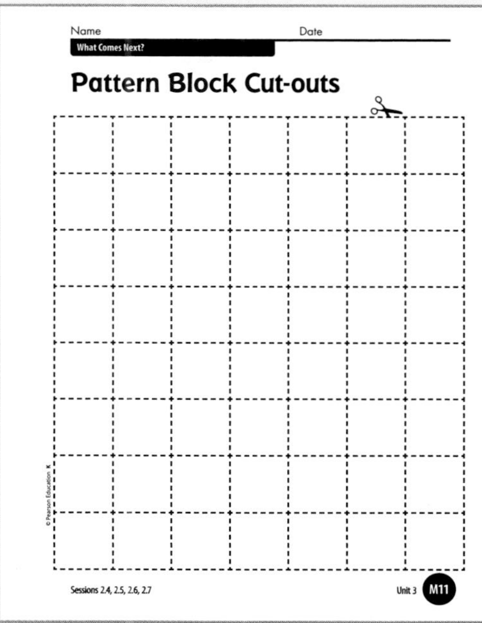

▲ Resource Masters, M11

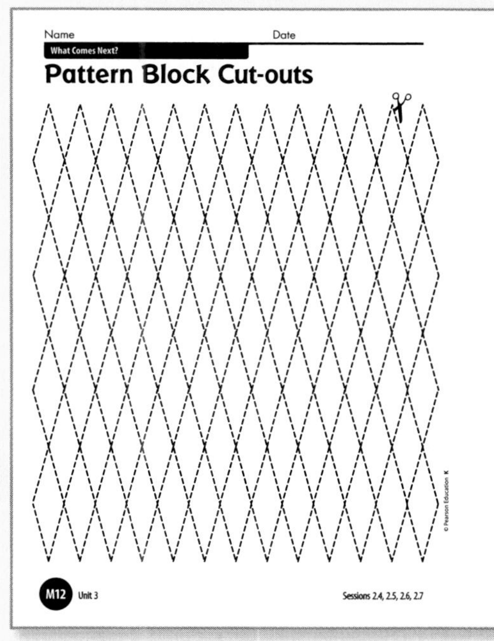

▲ Resource Masters, M12

One–Two Patterns

Math Focus Points

- Determining what comes next in a repeating pattern
- Constructing repeating patterns
- Recording repeating patterns

Vocabulary

same
different

Today's Plan		Materials
1 ACTIVITY **Introducing One–Two Patterns**	10 MIN CLASS	• Square tiles
2 MATH WORKSHOP **Constructing and Recording More Patterns** 2A One–Two Patterns 2B Pattern Block Snakes 2C Recording Cube Train Patterns	15–30 MIN	2A • Square tiles 2B • Materials from Session 2.4, p. 75 2C • Materials from Session 2.3, p. 70
3 DISCUSSION **Checking In**	5 MIN CLASS	
4 SESSION FOLLOW-UP **Homework**		• M13, Family Letter*

*See *Materials to Prepare,* p. 55.

Classroom Routines

Attendance: How Many Have Counted? **Count around the circle as usual, but pause several times during the count to ask students how many people have counted so far and how they know. Help students see why the number they say represents the number of students who have counted so far and that the last number represents the total number of students in class today.**

1 ACTIVITY

Introducing One–Two Patterns

10 MIN CLASS

Gather students so they can see a pattern made of square tiles. Alternatively, put the tiles on an overhead projector or sketch them on chart paper.

You've been using square tiles to make patterns this week. I'm going to make a pattern with square tiles.

Make a pattern, not based on color, where groups of one and two tiles alternate.①

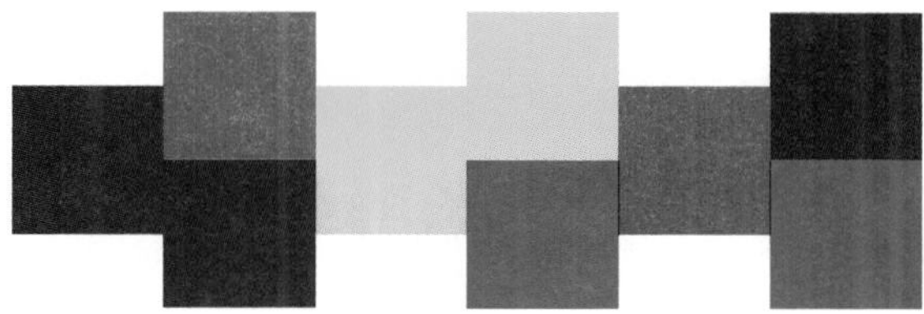

Here is a pattern I made with the square tiles. How would you describe my pattern?

Some students do not think this a pattern because the colors are not arranged in a repeating pattern. Others see a pattern in the shapes (i.e., square, rectangle, square, rectangle) or the sizes (i.e., small, big, small, big) the tiles make. Still others use numbers to describe the pattern: one, two, one, two.

When I made my pattern I did not pay attention to the color of the tiles. I could have made my pattern with all blue tiles or all yellow tiles or all different color tiles. I paid attention to something else. What do you think will come next in my pattern?

Students describe what the next element will look like in a variety of ways such as one tile, a square, or small. Extend the pattern together as a class by adding two or three more elements. Leave this pattern intact, so that students can compare it with the next pattern you make.

Do a second example with students. Make the following pattern:

Ask students to describe and extend it. Then, ask students to compare

Teaching Note

① **Hopscotch** You can use the game of hopscotch to introduce or extend one–two patterns. Demonstrate a pattern (e.g., hop on one foot, then two feet, then one foot, then two feet) and ask students to copy it. You can represent such patterns with 8-inch card stock or carpet squares. You can also build a pattern with squares and ask students to act it out. Students can then create their own paths with squares and take turns hopping them. For some students the physical movement involved in these patterns may help them make more sense of repeating patterns.

the two patterns.

How are these two patterns the same?

Students might say:

"They are both made of tiles."

"They both have one and two squares."

How are these two patterns different?

Students might say:

"This one has [green and yellow] tiles, and this one has [red and blue] tiles."

"This one goes small, tall, small, tall. This one goes small, then another small, and then tall."

You noticed a lot about how they are the same and different. In both of these patterns I put down either one tile by itself or two tiles next to each other. That's why we are going to call them one–two patterns.

My first pattern went one tile, two tiles, one tile, two tiles. My second pattern went one tile, one tile, two tiles, one tile, one tile, two tiles.

Explain that making One–Two Patterns will be one activity they can choose during Math Workshop. Remind them, that with One–Two Patterns, the color of the tiles does not matter.

MATH WORKSHOP

15–30 MIN

Constructing and Recording More Patterns

Explain that the following three activities are available during Math Workshop. Remind students what each activity entails, what materials are required, and where they are located.

2A One–Two Patterns

INDIVIDUALS

Students use square tiles, in groups of one or two, to make patterns.

ONGOING ASSESSMENT: Observing Students at Work

Students make repeating patterns using quantity as an attribute.

- **Are students able to make one–two patterns?** What types of patterns do they make?
- **How do students describe their patterns?** Do they refer to size? Shape? Orientation? Number?

DIFFERENTIATION: Supporting the Range of Learners

Intervention Some students make one–two patterns that are also color patterns while others struggle to make a one–two pattern because they have difficulty ignoring color as an attribute.

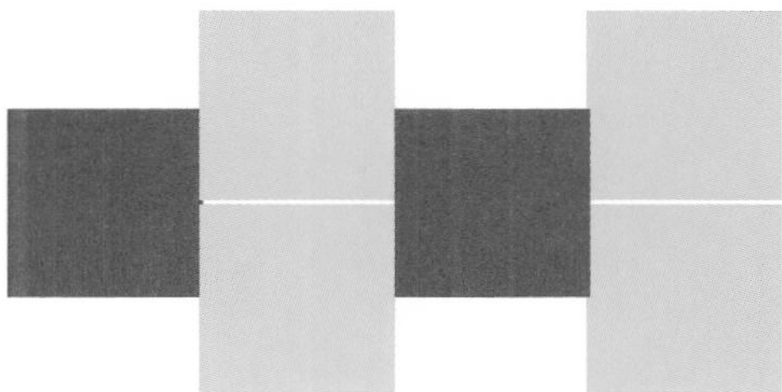

Remind students that the color of the tiles does not matter in one–two patterns. You might encourage these students to work initially with tiles of only one color.

2B Pattern Block Snakes

INDIVIDUALS

For complete details about this activity, see Session 2.4, page 77.

DIFFERENTIATION: Supporting the Range of Learners

Extension Challenge students who make and record simple patterns easily to construct more complicated patterns. For example, you can ask the question, "Can you use three different shapes to make a pattern block snake?"

2C Recording Cube Train Patterns

INDIVIDUALS

For complete details about this activity, see Session 2.3, page 73.

DIFFERENTIATION: Supporting the Range of Learners

Extension Challenge students who easily make and record simple patterns to construct more complicated patterns. For example, you can ask: "Can you use three different colors in your cube train?" Or, "What if the first three cubes in a train went blue, blue, orange? Can you finish my cube train?"

DISCUSSION

Checking In

Take this opportunity to discuss any issues that you noticed while observing students at work. The topic might be mathematical in nature, such as a common error or misconception (e.g., making patterns based on the color, rather than the number, of tiles) or a strategy (e.g., using tiles of one color to make one–two patterns) you'd like students to discuss.

The issue might also be logistical (e.g., taking apart patterns so that other students can use the materials) or management related (e.g., sharing materials or what to do when certain shapes are scarce).

Other alternatives include checking with students about which activities they have been choosing, asking students to share a piece of work, or allowing students to raise a question or make a comment about today's math class.

SESSION FOLLOW-UP

Homework

Family Letter: Send home a copy of Family Letter (M13) with each student.

SESSION 2.6

What Comes Next?

Math Focus Points

- Constructing and recording repeating patterns
- Copying repeating patterns
- Determining what comes next in a repeating pattern

Vocabulary

pattern

Today's Plan		Materials
❶ ACTIVITY Introducing *What Comes Next?*	5–10 MIN CLASS	• Teddy Bear or other counters; small opaque cups
❷ MATH WORKSHOP *What Comes Next?* and Recording Patterns 2A *What Comes Next?* 2B One-Two Patterns 2C Pattern Block Snakes 2D Recording Cube Train Patterns	20–30 MIN	2A • M4 (optional) • Teddy Bear or other counters; small opaque cups 2B • Materials from Session 2.5, p. 80 2C • Materials from Session 2.4, p. 75 2D • Materials from Session 2.3, p. 70
❸ DISCUSSION Checking In	5 MIN CLASS	
❹ SESSION FOLLOW-UP Practice		• *Student Activity Book*, p. 21

Classroom Routines

Today's Question: Would you rather drink apple juice or grape juice? **On chart paper, create a vertical two-column table titled "Would you rather drink apple juice or grape juice?" with the heading "Apple Juice" written at the top of one column and "Grape Juice" written at the top of the other column. Students respond by writing their names below the appropriate heading. Count the responses as a class and discuss what the results of the survey tell you.**

Teaching Notes

1 **Sneaking a Peek** Kindergarten students, in their eagerness to play the game, often peek while they are covering their eyes. Discuss this and generate some strategies for covering their eyes while their partners are building their patterns.

2 **Making Connections** Point out how this activity is a lot like *Patterns on the Pocket Chart* and the paper cups are similar to the Question Mark Cards.

5–10 MIN CLASS

ACTIVITY 1

Introducing *What Comes Next?*

Introduce *What Comes Next?* by playing a demonstration game with a volunteer.

In this game, one person makes a pattern with teddy bear counters and hides the last few bears under these cups.

In What Comes Next?, *students look at a pattern to determine what shape or object comes*

Ask your volunteer to cover his or her eyes. Make an AB pattern with 12 teddy bears, hiding each of the last four or five bears underneath a cup. Then invite your volunteer to look at your pattern.1

The first thing [Carmen] needs to do is build the part of my pattern that she can see. Then, [she] tries to figure out what color bears are underneath my cups. She has to guess what comes next in my pattern. [Touch the first cup] [Carmen], what do you think is under this cup? Why do you think so?2

Discuss your partner's guess and then reveal the bear under the cup.

[Carmen] thought this would be a red bear [Remove the cup] and [She's] right! So now [Carmen] adds a red bear to her pattern. And then [she] tries to guess what comes next—what color bear is under the next cup.

Continue this process until all of the bears in your pattern are revealed, and your partner has constructed a replica of your pattern.

As you play, you can make any kind of pattern, but you can use only two colors. Also, you should cover only the last four or five counters with cups, so your partner can see a lot of your pattern.

Play one more round, asking two student volunteers to demonstrate. Player 1 covers his or her eyes while the other makes a pattern and covers the last few bears. Player 2 copies the visible part of the pattern and figures out what comes next.

MATH WORKSHOP

What Comes Next? and Recording Patterns

20–30 MIN

Explain that the following four activities are available during Math Workshop. Remind students what each activity entails, what materials are required, and where they are located.

2A *What Comes Next?*

PAIRS

Player 1 uses two colors of teddy bear counters to make a pattern and then covers the last few bears with a small paper cup, while Player 2 is covering his or her eyes. Player 2 copies the pattern that is showing, figures out what comes next, and continues to copy the pattern as each element is revealed.

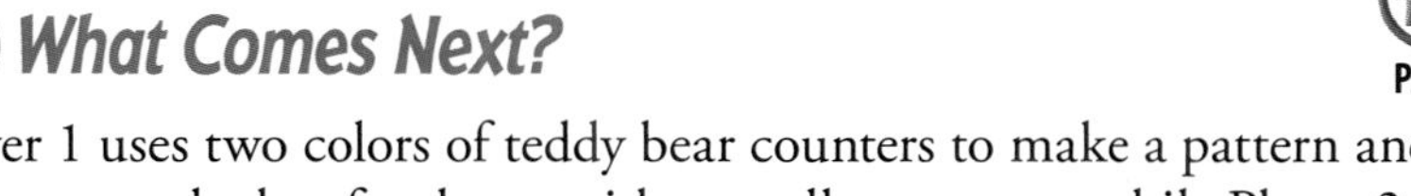

ONGOING ASSESSMENT: Observing Students at Work

Students make and copy patterns and determine what comes next in a pattern.

- **How do students construct patterns with two colors?** Do they always make an AB pattern? Or are they trying ABB patterns or AAB patterns?
- **Can students determine what comes next in the pattern?** Can they describe how they know what comes next?

Teaching Notes

3 **But That's Not a Pattern** Keep in mind that some students will construct a sequence of bears that is not a pattern. Talk with students about strategies for handling such situations respectfully.

4 **Don't Forget to Build It** Kindergarteners are eager to guess the next item in a pattern and reveal what is under the cup. Remind them that they need to build the pattern *before* they are permitted to guess what comes next.

Professional Development

5 **Dialogue Box:** A "Harder" Pattern, p. 163

DIFFERENTIATION: Supporting the Range of Learners

Intervention A Pattern Path (M4) may help some students organize their work.

Intervention As students are working, be particularly aware of those who may have difficulty making a pattern that repeats in a predictable way. You might be partners with such a student, deciding on a pattern together.

Intervention Some students strive to make a difficult pattern, cover up most of the pattern, or cover the pattern in a tricky way (e.g., covering every other bear). Be clear that the purpose of this activity is not to trick their partners, but to make a pattern that helps their partners figure out what comes next. 5

INDIVIDUALS

2B One-Two Patterns

For complete details about this activity, see Session 2.5, page 81.

DIFFERENTIATION: Supporting the Range of Learners

Extension Students who make a variety of one-two patterns with tiles can explore one-two patterns with other materials (e.g., pattern blocks). You can also challenge them to construct patterns that include groups of 3 or 4 tiles.

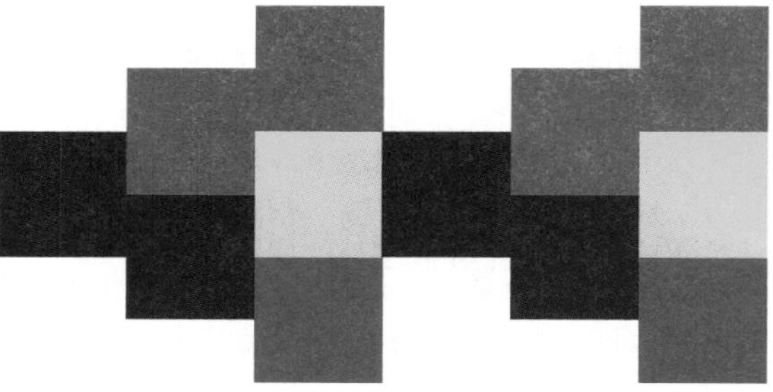

INDIVIDUALS

2C Pattern Block Snakes

For complete details about this activity, see Session 2.4, page 77.

INDIVIDUALS

2D Recording Cube Train Patterns

For complete details about this activity, see Session 2.3, page 73.

DISCUSSION

Checking In

Take this opportunity to discuss any issues that you noticed while observing students at work. The problem of what to do when someone makes a non-pattern in *What Comes Next?* would be a useful topic to check on. Together, brainstorm ways to handle this.

Otherwise you might talk about a mathematical (e.g., strategies for figuring out what comes next in someone's pattern or what made a particular pattern "hard") or logistical (e.g., not looking while your partner constructs a pattern) issue that arose.

Other alternatives include checking with students about which activities they have been choosing (e.g., "Thumbs up if you worked on *What Comes Next?* Thumbs up if you worked on one–two patterns."), asking everyone to hold up a piece of work, or allowing students to raise a question or make a comment about that day's math class.

SESSION FOLLOW-UP

Practice

Practice: For reinforcement of this unit's content, have students complete *Student Activity Book* page 21.

Name Date

What Comes Next?

Practice

What Comes Next?

Draw what comes next if the pattern continues.

NOTE Students practice extending repeating patterns.

Session 2.6 Unit 3 21

▲ Student Activity Book, p. 21

SESSION 2.7

Is It a Pattern?

Math Focus Points

- Constructing and recording repeating patterns
- Determining what comes next in a repeating pattern
- Distinguishing between patterns and non-patterns

Today's Plan		Materials
1 ACTIVITY **Introducing Recording Two-Color Counter Patterns**	5 MIN CLASS	• M14* • 12 two-color counters; red and yellow crayons
2 MATH WORKSHOP **What Comes Next? and Recording More Patterns** 2A Recording Two-Color Counter Patterns 2B *What Comes Next?* 2C One–Two Patterns 2D Pattern Block Snakes 2E Recording Cube Train Patterns	15–30 MIN	2A • M14 • Materials from Session 2.1, p. 58 • Red and yellow crayons; tape (optional) 2B • Materials from Session 2.6, p. 85 2C • Materials from Session 2.5, p. 80; paper strips and colored paper squares* 2D • Materials from Session 2.4, p. 75 2E • Materials from Session 2.3, p. 70
3 DISCUSSION **Is This a Pattern?**	10 MIN CLASS	• Non-pattern snake*
4 SESSION FOLLOW-UP **Practice**		• *Student Math Handbook Flip Chart,* pp. 41, 42

*See *Materials to Prepare,* p. 55.

Classroom Routines

Patterns on the Pocket Chart **Arrange an ABC repeating pattern on the pocket chart using 10 pattern blocks (blue rhombus, red trapezoid, orange square). Follow the basic *Patterns* activity. Students hold up the block that they think is under the first Question Mark Card.**

ACTIVITY

5 MIN CLASS

Introducing Recording Two-Color Counter Patterns

Explain that two-color counters will be available again today for making patterns. This time, students will also record their patterns. Make a pattern with 12 two-color counters and ask students to describe it. Then show them a Two-Color Counter Strip (M14).

How could I use red and yellow crayons and this strip to record my pattern?

Students might say:

"We could make the pattern on top of it and put the chips in the circles, and then color them as we take them off."

"Put the strip next to the pattern and copy it."

Those are good suggestions. As you record, remember that, just like the cube strips, if your pattern is shorter than the strip, you have to color in only as many circles as there are in your pattern.

Some students may want to tape two strips together to record longer patterns.

MATH WORKSHOP

15–30 MIN

What Comes Next? and Recording More Patterns

Explain that five activities are available during Math Workshop. Remind students what each activity entails, what materials are required and where they are located. This is the last day for Pattern Block Snakes.

INDIVIDUALS

2A Recording Two-Color Counter Patterns

Students make and record patterns made with two-color counters.

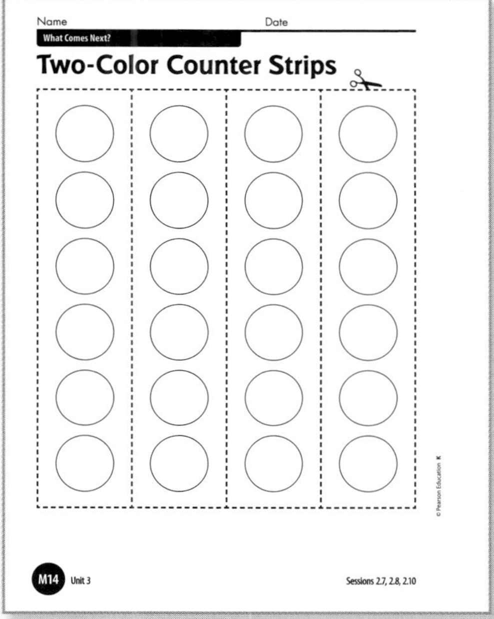

Name Date

What Comes Next?

Two-Color Counter Strips

M14 Unit 3 Sessions 2.7, 2.8, 2.10

© Pearson Education K

▲ Resource Masters, M14

ONGOING ASSESSMENT: Observing Students at Work

Students make and record repeating patterns.

- **Are students able to make a pattern with two-color counters?** What kinds of patterns do they make?
- **How do students record their patterns?** Does what they record match their pattern? Do they double-check?

DIFFERENTIATION: Supporting the Range of Learners

Intervention Work with students who have difficulty accurately recording their pattern to model strategies the class suggested, such as lining up the chips and the strip or building the pattern on the strip.

If there are students who seem overwhelmed by the recording aspect and are still working to construct arrangements that are patterns, ask them to continue making patterns. Ask them to record as they seem ready.

2B *What Comes Next?*

PAIRS

For complete details about this activity, see Session 2.6, page 87.

DIFFERENTIATION: Supporting the Range of Learners

Extension Challenge students who can easily make and extend AB patterns to work with other kinds of patterns. You can also challenge students by pointing to a cup toward the end of the pattern and asking, "What comes here?"

Some students may be ready to determine the missing shape or object that comes later in the pattern.

2C One–Two Patterns

INDIVIDUALS

For complete details about this activity, see Session 2.5, page 81.

DIFFERENTIATION: Supporting the Range of Learners

Extension Students who are ready for more challenge can record their one–two patterns. They'll need a strip of blank paper and paper squares that match the colors of the tiles.

2D Pattern Block Snakes

INDIVIDUALS

For complete details about this activity, see Session 2.4, page 77.

2E Recording Cube Train Patterns

INDIVIDUALS

For complete details about this activity, see Session 2.3, page 73.

3 DISCUSSION
Is This a Pattern?

10 MIN CLASS

Math Focus Points for Discussion

- Distinguishing between patterns and non-patterns

Show students an AB pattern snake that one of the students made.

Here is a pattern block snake that [Mia] made. This is what her snake looks like: [triangle, hexagon, triangle, hexagon, triangle, hexagon, triangle, hexagon, triangle]. Is this snake a pattern? Why do you think so?

Students might say:

"It is a pattern because it goes over and over again: triangle, hexagon, triangle, hexagon."

"It's a pattern because it has the same two colors over and over again."

Math Note

1 **That's Not a Pattern** Some students say that non-AB patterns are "like" patterns, but they do not consider them true patterns. Although they may agree that such arrangements repeat over and over again, they may think the word *pattern* encompasses only AB patterns. Some students may have difficulty seeing the repetition in a non-AB pattern. As they gain more experience with a wide variety of patterns, they will become more comfortable with this idea.

If she was going to make her snake longer, what would come next in the snake? Why do you think so?

Show students another snake that is an ABB or AAB pattern.

Here is another snake. Do you think it is a pattern? Why do you think so? Remember that patterns have something that **repeats** over and over. 1

Encourage students to explain their thinking.

Finally, show students the snake you made with two colors that is not a pattern.

Here is a snake I made. Do you think it is a pattern? Why do you think so?

Some students think it is a pattern because it has two colors. Others say it is not because it changes or because you can't tell what comes next.

If something is a pattern, we should be able to tell what comes next. If I were going to make my snake longer, can we tell what would come next? Why or why not?

End by asking students to help you figure out how you could change your snake to make it a pattern. Use pattern blocks to model different ideas students suggest, which may include AB, AAB, ABB, and even AABB patterns.

SESSION FOLLOW-UP

Practice

Student Math Handbook Flip Chart: Use the *Student Math Handbook Flip Chart* pages 41, 42 to reinforce concepts from this unit. See pages 165–166 in the back of this unit.

Arrow Patterns

Math Focus Points

- Describing repeating patterns
- Determining what comes next in a repeating pattern
- Constructing and recording repeating patterns

Today's Plan		Materials
1 ACTIVITY **Introducing Arrow Patterns on the Pocket Chart**	10 MIN CLASS	• M15* • Materials from Session 2.2, p. 65
2 MATH WORKSHOP **Patterns with Directions and Numbers** 2A Arrow Patterns 2B *What Comes Next?* 2C One–Two Patterns 2D Recording Two-Color Counter Patterns	15–30 MIN	2A • M16* 2B • Materials from Session 2.6, p. 85 2C • Materials from Session 2.5, p. 80 2D • Materials from Session 2.7, p. 90
3 DISCUSSION **Checking In**	5 MIN CLASS	
4 SESSION FOLLOW-UP **Practice**		• *Student Math Handbook Flip Chart,* pp. 41, 42

*See *Materials to Prepare,* p. 57.

Classroom Routines

Patterns on the Pocket Chart **Arrange an ABC repeating pattern on the pocket chart using ten arrow cards (up, down, left). Follow the basic *Patterns* activity. Students point in the direction they think is under each Question Mark Card.**

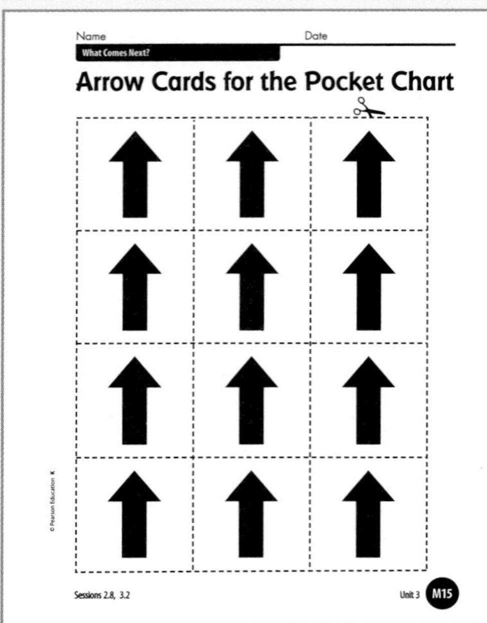
Name Date

What Comes Next?

Arrow Cards for the Pocket Chart

© Pearson Education K

Sessions 2.8, 3.2 Unit 3 M15

▲ Resource Masters, M15

ACTIVITY

10 MIN CLASS

Introducing Arrow Patterns on the Pocket Chart

Gather students so they can see the pocket chart. Secretly, make a pattern with ten Arrow Cards for the Pocket Chart (M15) in the first row. Orient the cards to make the following AB pattern: down arrow, up arrow, down arrow, up arrow, and so on. Cover the last three or four arrows with Question Mark Cards (M5).

Today I used arrows to make a pattern on our pocket chart. Take a look. I'm wondering how we could use our bodies to show this pattern.

Have students share and model their ideas, which might include standing and then sitting; pointing up and then down; raising and then lowering their hands, arms, knees, or legs; or looking up and then looking down. Model students' ideas, and encourage the whole group to act them out as well.

Students follow an Arrow Pattern using body movements.

What do you think will come next in this pattern? Show with your body which way you think the next arrow will be pointing.

Reveal the first covered card. Continue in this way until the whole pattern is revealed. Ask students what the pattern will look like if it continues.

If time permits, do another pattern: left arrow, down arrow, down arrow, left arrow, down arrow, down arrow, and so on. Cover the last three or four arrows with Question Mark Cards, and follow the same process.

Today, one of the choices will be making arrow patterns during Math Workshop.

15–30 MIN

MATH WORKSHOP

Patterns with Directions and Numbers

Explain that the following four activities are available during Math Workshop. Remind students what each activity entails, what materials are required, and where they are located.

INDIVIDUALS

2A Arrow Patterns

Students use Arrow Cards (M16) to make patterns.

ONGOING ASSESSMENT: Observing Students at Work

Students make patterns using directionality.

- **Can students make arrow patterns?** What kinds of patterns do they construct?
- **How do students describe their patterns?** Do they use direction words? Do they use their bodies to illustrate?

DIFFERENTIATION: Supporting the Range of Learners

Intervention Some students have difficulty with directionality as an attribute, as opposed to color, shape, or other attributes. Encourage these students to begin by making a pattern with only arrows facing up or down. They may also benefit from first acting out a pattern with their bodies and then using the Arrow Cards to represent their patterns.

As you talk with students, encourage them to describe and act out their patterns. Occasionally act out a student's pattern and ask students to reflect on whether you have accurately modeled the pattern.

PAIRS

2B *What Comes Next?*

For complete details about this activity, see Session 2.6, page 87.

INDIVIDUALS

2C One-Two Patterns

For complete details about this activity, see Session 2.5, page 81.

INDIVIDUALS

2D Recording Two-Color Counter Patterns

For complete details about this activity, see Session 2.7, page 91.

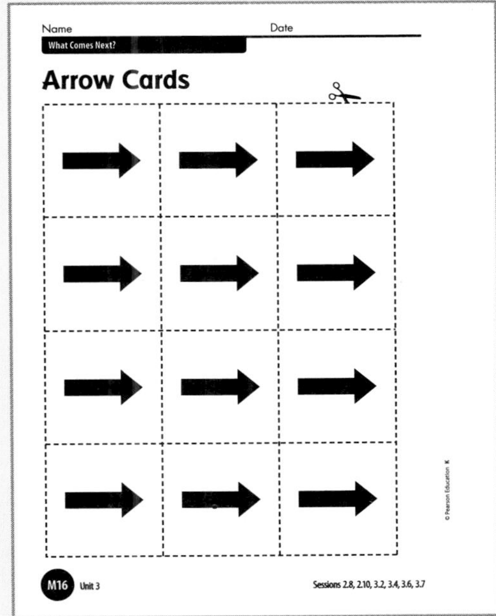
Name Date

What Comes Next?

Arrow Cards

M16 Unit 3

Sessions 2.8, 2.10, 3.2, 3.4, 3.6, 3.7

▲ Resource Masters, M16

DISCUSSION

Checking In

Take this opportunity to discuss any issues you noticed while observing students at work. The topic might be mathematical in nature, such as a strategy you'd like all students to consider (e.g., strategies for accurately recording patterns) or a common error or misconception you'd like students to discuss (e.g., making a line of arrows that is not a pattern). It could also be a management issue (e.g., where to store the patterns they recorded on paper, or making choices and working productively during Math Workshop).

Other alternatives include checking in with students about which activities they have been choosing (e.g., "Thumbs up if you worked on arrow patterns today. Thumbs up if you played *What Comes Next?* Thumbs up if you recorded a pattern you made."), asking everyone to hold up a piece of work, or allowing students to raise a question or make a comment about today's math class.

SESSION FOLLOW-UP

Practice

Student Math Handbook Flip Chart: Use the *Student Math Handbook Flip Chart* pages 41, 42 to reinforce concepts from today's session. See pages 165–166 in the back of this unit.

Add On

Math Focus Points

- Determining what comes next in a repeating pattern
- Constructing repeating patterns
- Counting 12 objects

Today's Plan			Materials
ACTIVITY 1 Introducing *Add On*	5–10 MIN	CLASS	• 1-to-2 dot cubes*; connecting cubes (1 bin)
ACTIVITY 2 Playing *Add On*	15–25 MIN	CLASS	• 1-to-2 dot cubes*; connecting cubes; stick-on dots
DISCUSSION 3 Adding On	10 MIN	CLASS	• 1-to-2 dot cubes*; connecting cubes
SESSION FOLLOW-UP 4 Practice			• *Student Math Handbook Flip Chart,* pp. 40, 41

*See *Materials to Prepare,* p. 57.

Classroom Routines

Calendar: Days of the Week **Use the calendar to review the days of the week, noting which days are school days and which are weekend (or non-school) days.**

ACTIVITY

Introducing *Add On*

Show students the materials needed to play *Add On*—a bin of connecting cubes and a 1-to-2 dot cube—and ask a volunteer to play a demonstration game with you.

The object of *Add On* is to use two colors to make a pattern that has 12 cubes in it. First, [Mary] and I each need to choose a color. [Mary] chose blue, and I chose yellow. To start the game, we each take one of our cubes and snap them together. [Mary] and I are going to be working together to make a pattern that goes blue, yellow, blue, yellow.

You and your partner take turns rolling the 1-to-2 cube to find how many cubes to add.[Have Mary roll the cube.] [Mary] rolled a [1]. So [she] needs to add [one] cube to our blue/yellow cube pattern. What color cube does [Mary] need to add? How do you know?

Now our pattern is blue, yellow, blue. I rolled a [2]. What color cubes should I take? Which should I add first, the blue or the yellow? How do you know?

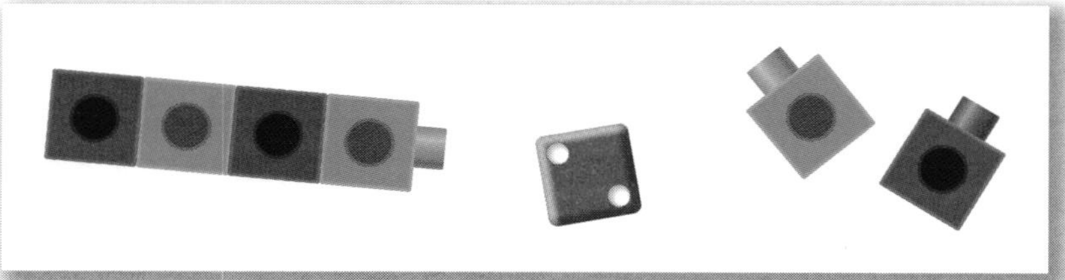

Continue taking turns, asking students to help you figure out what color cubes to take and to explain how they know. Remind them that the goal is to build a train with 12 cubes and occasionally ask whether students think you have 12 yet.

We want to make a pattern with 12 cubes. Do we have enough cubes yet? How many more cubes will we need before we have 12?

Explain that once students have 12 cubes in their train they should check to make sure they have made a pattern. They then choose two new colors and play another game.

ACTIVITY

2 Playing *Add On*

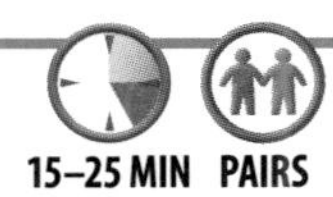

15–25 MIN PAIRS

Students play *Add On* in pairs. They choose two colors to make an AB pattern. They take turns rolling a 1-to-2 dot cube and adding that number of cubes to their train until they have 12 cubes in their pattern.

ONGOING ASSESSMENT: Observing Students at Work

Students make and extend an AB pattern.

- **Are students able to make and extend an AB pattern?** Are they comfortable adding on, no matter what the color of the last cube is? Or do students struggle when the last cube is not the last cube of the unit (e.g., when the last cube is blue in a blue-yellow pattern)?
- **How do students figure out what comes next?** Do they say the colors in the pattern aloud from the first cube? Do they look only at the last one or two cubes? Do they just know that after [blue] comes [yellow]?
- **Do students recognize when a mistake has been made?** Can they fix it?

DIFFERENTIATION: Supporting the Range of Learners

Intervention In working together to build one cube train, some students become confused about where the train begins. Suggest that these students place a stick-on dot on the first cube of their train.

DISCUSSION
3 Adding On

Math Focus Points for Discussion

- Constructing repeating patterns
- Determining what comes next in a repeating pattern

Make an AB pattern with four cubes.

Suppose I was playing *Add On* and so far my partner and I had built this pattern. Now I am going to roll the dot cube. I rolled a [2]. What color cubes do I need? What should I add on first? How do you know?

Some students say the colors from the beginning of the pattern; others know "because you have to put on a cube that's a different color next."

I noticed that when [Ricardo] had to add a cube to [his] pattern, [he] said all the colors in the pattern from the beginning, and this helped [him] figure out what to add on. Who else used this strategy? Let's try this strategy.

Use the strategy to decide which color cube to add next. Then ask whether anyone used a different strategy, and use it to check that you added the correct color cube.

Roll the dot cube a few more times, asking students what cubes to add and to explain how they know. Try the strategies students suggest.

SESSION FOLLOW-UP
4 Practice

Student Math Handbook Flip Chart: Use the *Student Math Handbook Flip Chart* pages 40, 41 to reinforce concepts from this unit. See pages 165–166 in the back of this unit.

SESSION 2.10

Sharing Patterns

Math Focus Points

- Constructing repeating patterns
- Determining what comes next in a repeating pattern
- Recording repeating patterns

Today's Plan		Materials
1 ACTIVITY **Introducing *Add On* with Other Materials**	5 MIN CLASS	• 1-to-2 dot cube; connecting cubes; pattern blocks; two-color counters
2 MATH WORKSHOP **Extending, Constructing, and Recording Patterns** 2A *Add On:* Cubes, Pattern Blocks, and Two-Color Counters 2B Arrow Patterns 2C Recording Two-Color Counter Patterns 2D *What Comes Next?* 2E One–Two Patterns	10–25 MIN	2A • Materials from Session 2.9, p. 99; pattern blocks; two-color counters 2B • Materials from Session 2.8, p. 95; extra Arrow Cards (optional); glue (optional) 2C • Materials from Session 2.7, p. 90 2D • Materials from Session 2.6, p. 85 2E • Materials from Session 2.5, p. 80
3 ACTIVITY **Choosing a Favorite Pattern**	5 MIN INDIVIDUALS	• Folder of student work
4 DISCUSSION **Sharing Patterns**	10 MIN CLASS	• Students' recorded patterns
5 SESSION FOLLOW UP **Practice**		• *Student Math Handbook Flip Chart,* pp. 41, 42

Classroom Routines

Attendance: What if We Start With. . . ? **Count around the circle as usual to determine the total number of students present today. Then ask students what they think would happen if the count began with a different student and why. Choose a different student to start, count again, and discuss what happens.**

ACTIVITY

Introducing *Add On* with Other Materials

Today if you play *Add On*, you can play with cubes, just like you did yesterday. But you can also choose to play with pattern blocks or two-color counters.

Play a few rounds of *Add On* with the pattern blocks. Tell students that, just as with the cubes, each players needs to choose a shape and that the pattern will alternate the two shapes they choose.

Also model a few rounds of *Add On* with the two-color counters.

MATH WORKSHOP

10–25 MIN

Extending, Constructing, and Recording Patterns

Explain that the following five activities are available during Math Workshop. Remind students what each activity entails, what materials are required, and where they are located.

For complete details about this activity, see Session 2.9, page 100.

Extension Students who are ready for more variation can play *Add On* with pattern blocks or two-color counters instead of cubes.

You can also challenge students to begin with three cubes, of either two or three different colors, at the beginning of the game. They build a train with those three cubes, and then play as usual, rolling the cube to determine how many additional cubes to add on. In this variation, they will be extending an ABC, AAB, or ABB pattern.

2B Arrow Patterns

INDIVIDUALS

For complete details about this activity, see Session 2.8, page 96.

DIFFERENTIATION: Supporting the Range of Learners

Extension Some students might like to record their arrow patterns by gluing down paper copies of the Arrow Cards. Others will attempt to draw their pattern directly on paper.

2C Recording Two-Color Counter Patterns

INDIVIDUALS

For complete details about this activity, see Session 2.7, page 91.

2D *What Comes Next?*

PAIRS

For complete details about this activity, see Session 2.6, page 87.

2E One-Two Patterns

INDIVIDUALS

For complete details about this activity, see Session 2.5, page 81.

3 ACTIVITY
Choosing a Favorite Pattern

5 MIN

INDIVIDUALS

You are going to share a pattern you made. This session will end with a discussion about the patterns you've been recording. Take a few minutes to choose your favorite pattern from your work folder.

DISCUSSION

4 Sharing Patterns

10 MIN CLASS

Math Focus Points for Discussion

- Determining what comes next in a repeating pattern

Ask students to bring their favorite recorded pattern to the discussion. Or, ask them to display them at their workspace, and have children walk around the classroom and view them as if in a museum.

Students share their recorded repeating patterns.

Have all of the students who chose a pattern block snake hold up their patterns. Ask students individually to briefly describe their patterns, and give the rest of the class time to comment on what they notice about the pattern block snakes. Follow the same process with each kind of pattern represented (e.g., cube train patterns, two-color counter patterns, tile or arrow patterns).

As children share, occasionally choose a pattern and ask:

Here is [Mary's] cube train pattern. Can someone describe it for us?

Students might say:

"It goes [red, white, blue, red, white, blue]."

If [Mary's] pattern continued in the same way, what would come next? How do you know?

Students might say:

"[Red] would come next because the pattern is [red, white, blue]. It's always red first."

After the discussion, collect the patterns and post them as part of your classroom's Pattern Display.

SESSION FOLLOW-UP

Practice

Student Math Handbook Flip Chart: Use the *Student Math Handbook Flip Chart* pages 41, 42 to reinforce concepts from this unit. See pages 165–166 in the back of this unit.

INVESTIGATION 3

Mathematical Emphases

Repeating Patterns Constructing, describing, and extending repeating patterns

Math Focus Points

- ◆ Constructing repeating patterns
- ◆ Constructing a variety of patterns using the same elements
- ◆ Comparing different kinds of patterns

Repeating Patterns Identifying the unit of a repeating pattern

Math Focus Points

- ◆ Identifying the unit of a repeating pattern
- ◆ Counting the number of units in a repeating pattern
- ◆ Extending a repeating pattern by adding on units to the pattern

---

This Investigation also focuses on

- ◆ Counting, creating, and representing quantities

What's the Unit?

	Student Activity Book	Student Math Handbook Flip Chart	Professional Development: Read Ahead of Time
SESSION 3.1 p. 114			
Break the Train Student pairs take turns constructing 2-color cube train patterns and breaking them down into two-cube units or "cars." They discuss how to show on paper the cars and the number of cars.	22	43	• **Teacher Note:** What's the Unit?, p. 152 • **Dialogue Box:** *Break the Train,* p. 153
SESSION 3.2 p. 119			
Recording Break the Train In Math Workshop, students construct and extend patterns and identify and record the part of the pattern that repeats. The session ends with a discussion of how to break an AAB pattern into units.	22	43	
SESSION 3.3 p. 124			
How Many Cars? Students are introduced to the game *How Many Cars?* in which they build a cube train pattern from a given unit and a given number of units. In Math Workshop they continue to extend patterns, identify the unit in a pattern, and work on the Counting Jar.	22	43	
SESSION 3.4 p. 129			
Break the Train with Other Materials Students learn how to play *Break the Train* with other materials: they construct patterns with other materials and then identify the unit. Math Workshop focuses on identifying the unit of a pattern. At the end of the session, they discuss the Counting Jar.	22, 23		

Classroom Routines See page 18 for an overview.

Today's Question

- Today's Question charts for Sessions 3.1 and 3.5. See instructions on pages 114 and 134.

Attendance

- No materials needed

Patterns on the Pocket Chart

- Pocket Chart(s) or Sentence Pocket Chart
- Question Mark Cards
- Arrow Cards for the Pocket Chart
- Pattern Blocks

Calendar

- Monthly calendar or class pocket calendar

Materials to Gather	Materials to Prepare
• **Connecting cubes** (1 tub per 3 to 4 students) • **Crayons** (same colors as cubes)	• **M17, Assessment Checklist: Identifying the Unit of a Pattern** ✓ Make copies. (4–5 per class) • **M18, *Break the Train* Recording Sheet** Make copies.(as needed) • **Train Cube Pattern** Construct an AB cube train pattern that is 12 cubes long.
• **Connecting cubes** (1 tub per 3 to 4 students) • **Crayons** (same colors as cubes) • **Materials for *Break the Train*** See Session 3.1. • **Materials for the Counting Jar** (as you have set it up) • **Materials for *Add On*** See Session 2.10, p. 103. • **Materials for Arrow Patterns** See Session 2.8, p. 95.	• **Counting Jar** Place 7 large objects inside (e.g., tennis balls, large Geoblocks).
• **Connecting cubes** (1 tub per 3 to 4 students) • **1-to-6 number cube** (1 per pair) • **Materials for *Break the Train*** See Session 3.1. • **Materials for the Counting Jar** See Session 3.2. • **Materials for *Add On*** See Session 2.10, p. 104.	• **M19, Car Cards** Make 6 copies. Color different combinations according to the colors of the connecting cubes. Cut each sheet apart to make one set. (6 sets per class)
• **Pattern blocks** (1 container per 3–4 students) • **Arrow Cards** (about 20 per student) • **Toothpicks** (about 10 per student) • **Two-color counters** • **Materials for *How Many Cars?*** See Session 3.3. • **Materials for *Break the Train*** See Session 3.1. • **Materials for the Counting Jar** See Session 3.2.	

✓ Checklist Available

What's the Unit?, *continued*

	Student Activity Book	Student Math Handbook Flip Chart	Professional Development: Read Ahead of Time
SESSION 3.5 p. 134 **12 Chips** Students make a variety of patterns using a total of 12 red and yellow chips. They mark the units in the pattern and count the number of units in each of their patterns. At the end of the session, they share and compare the variety of patterns they constructed with 12 two-color counters.	24	43	
SESSION 3.6 p. 138 **End-of-Unit Assessment and Comparing Patterns** As a class, students construct patterns on the Pocket Chart using a given unit. Then, while Math Workshop continues, students who have not yet met the benchmarks for this unit meet individually with the teacher. Class discussion focuses on comparing different kinds of patterns.	25		
SESSION 3.7 p. 143 **More End-of-Unit Assessment and the Pattern Display** Students identify the unit in patterns they make using body motions. Math Workshop continues, while students who have not yet met the benchmarks meet individually with the teacher. At the end of the session, students discuss and compare the items in the Pattern Display.		39, 43	

Materials to Gather	Materials to Prepare
• **Two-color counters** (12 per student) • **Chart paper**	• **M20, 12 Chips Recording Sheet** Make copies. (as needed) • **Red and yellow paper circles** Cut large circles from red and yellow construction paper so that they can be taped to the front of the classroom during the 12 Chips demonstration. (1 of each color per student)
• **Chart paper with 12 Chips patterns** (from Session 3.5) • **Pocket 100 chart** • **Pattern blocks** (1 tub) • **Question Mark Cards** (from Investigation 2) • **Connecting cubes** (1 tub) • **Materials for 12 Chips** See Session 3.5. • **Materials for *Break the Train* with Other Materials** See Session 3.4. • **Materials for *How Many Cars?*** See Session 3.3. • **Completed copies of Assessment Checklists** M3, M17 ✓	• **M3, M17 ✓, Assessment Checklists** Make copies. (as needed; from Sessions 1.5, 3.1) • **Prepared cube trains** Construct two or three different AB cube train patterns, one ABC cube train pattern and two cube trains that have assorted colors in a non-repeating arrangement. Use these for the assessment activity. • **Prepared cube trains** Construct five cube trains each 10 cubes long: one that has assorted colors in a non-repeating arrangement, two that are AB patterns, one that is an ABB pattern using the same colors as one of the AB patterns, and one that is an ABC pattern. Use these for the discussion.
• **Materials for End-of-Unit Assessments** See Session 3.6. • **Materials for 12 Chips** See Session 3.5. • **Materials for *Break the Train* with Other Materials** See Session 3.4. • **Materials for *How Many Cars?*** See Session 3.3. • **The Pattern Display** (from Sessions 2.1–2.7)	

✓ Checklist Available

Break the Train

Math Focus Points

- Identifying the unit of a repeating pattern
- Constructing repeating patterns
- Counting the number of units in a repeating pattern

Vocabulary

repeat

Today's Plan			Materials
ACTIVITY **1 Introducing *Break the Train***	5–10 MIN	CLASS	• Connecting cubes
ACTIVITY **2 Playing *Break the Train***	15–25 MIN	CLASS	• M17* ☑ • Connecting cubes
DISCUSSION **3 Recording *Break the Train***	10 MIN	CLASS	• *Student Activity Book,* p. 22 • M18* • Cube train pattern*; crayons
SESSION FOLLOW-UP **4 Practice**			• *Student Math Handbook Flip Chart,* p. 43

*See *Materials to Prepare,* p. 111.

Classroom Routines

Today's Question: Do you play an instrument? **On chart paper, create a vertical two-column table titled, "Do you play an instrument?" with the column heading "Yes" or "No" written at the bottom of each column. Students respond by writing their names above the appropriate heading. Count the responses as a class, and discuss what the results of the survey tell you. Ask students whether there are ways to organize the data so that it is easier to tell which group has more.**

Do more people play an instrument or more people not play an instrument? How can you tell? Is there something we could do next time, to make it easier to tell which group has more people in it?

If students suggest writing names one [over/under] the other, or drawing lines on the chart, try this the next time you do *Today's Question.*

ACTIVITY

5–10 MIN CLASS

Introducing *Break the Train*

Show students the cube train pattern you constructed. Ask the group to count the number of cubes in your train and then to say each color in the pattern as you point to each cube.

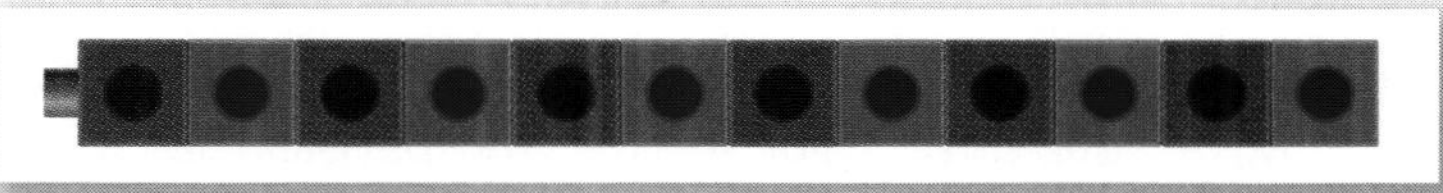

What is it that repeats in this pattern? What part comes back over and over and over again?

As you gather responses, ask students to explain their reasoning. It may not be obvious to everyone that [brown-red] is the unit that repeats over and over again.

If students have a hard time understanding your question, you might want to look with them at the cube train, cube by cube:

So the first cube is [brown] and the next one is [red]. Did the pattern start over again yet? . . . OK, now the next one is [brown], so we have [brown, red, brown]. What about now? Did anything repeat yet? . . . [Student] says the [brown] cube is the beginning of the repeat. Where's the next cube that starts another repeat?

To help students see the units that repeat, break apart the train into six individual units of [brown and red].

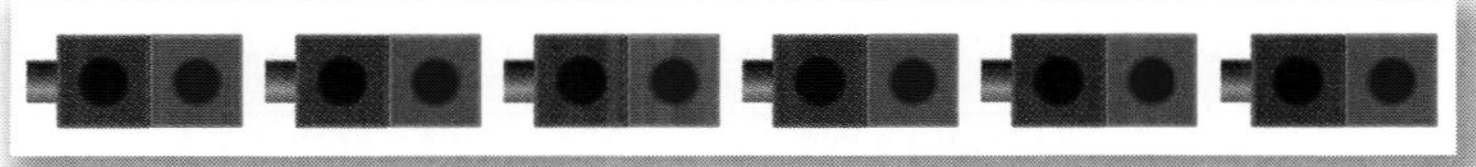

These cubes are like a train. Each car of my train is [brown and red]. I can make my train longer by adding on more [brown and red] cars. How many [brown and red] cars are in my train?❶ ❷ ❸

Together with students, count the number of [brown and red] cars (6). Then, snap the cars back together to form one long train.

Construct another 12-cube AB train pattern. Ask the students to help you break it down into cars.

What is it that repeats in this pattern? What part goes over and over and over again? What are the cars of this train?

Teaching Note

❶ **Units or "Cars"** The unit of a pattern is the part of a pattern that repeats over and over again. In *Break the Train* with cubes, students break their trains into units or "cars." The vocabulary of "trains" and "cars" may help some students begin to develop an image of what a unit is. Later in this Investigation students will be introduced to the word *unit,* as the mathematical term for cars.

Professional Development

❷ **Teacher Note:** What's the Unit?, p. 152

Differentiation

❸ **English Language Learners** English Language Learners may not be familiar with the words *train* and *car.* To clarify, draw a simple sketch of a train with several cars. This is a *train.* These are the *cars* of the train. All the cars connect to make one long train. Then sketch another train, in which each car is made up of a red square and a brown square. We're going to pretend that each car of the train has two colors. I chose red and brown for my cars. Then help students replicate the cars of the train sketch with snap cubes. Let's use snap cubes to build a train that looks like this one. Which two cubes can you put together to make a car?

Once you have broken the train down into cars, ask students to describe the cars.

What are the colors in each car? Is each car the same?

Then count together the number of cars.

Today, you and a partner will work on making pattern trains and breaking them into cars. Each of you chooses two colors for the cars of your own train. You need to make your train 12 cubes long. When you have made your train, trade it with your partner. See whether your partner can break your train into cars. Then, after you have broken a train into cars, see whether you can put it back together again.④

Put back together one of the two trains you constructed and save it for the discussion at the end of this session.⑤

2 ACTIVITY
Playing *Break the Train*

15–25 MIN CLASS

Students construct cube train patterns that are 12 cubes long using two colors and then break down the train their partners have made into units or "cars." After they have checked each other's work, they put the trains back together again.

Ask students to save one of the cube train patterns that they make during this time.⑥ ⑦

Assessment Checklist: Identifying the Unit of a Pattern

Student	Breaks a pattern into units	Constructs a pattern from a known unit	Notes
Emma	Yes breaks AB pattern into units and breaks AAB into z cube units—not correct	yes for AB patterns turns AAB car into AB pattern	
Jae	Yes for different kinds of patterns	yes	even for AAAB patterns
Brad	yes	no—needs to add one cube on at time not unit loses track of pattern	
Lisa	no	no	can make own pattern, can't identify units
Rebecca	yes AB patterns only	yes—for any pattern	

Teaching Note

④ **Two-Color Cube Trains** Because understanding the unit of a pattern is a challenging idea, we strongly recommend that students begin with units of two colors. Once students are comfortable with the idea of a unit, you can vary the difficulty by suggesting that they work with more colors in their pattern units.

⑥ **Assessing Students as They Identify the Unit of a Pattern** By the end of this unit, students are expected to be able to begin to identify the unit of the pattern that repeats (Benchmark 2). This means that they can break a pattern into units and construct a pattern from a known unit. Use M17, Assessment Checklist: Identifying the Unit of a Pattern to keep track of your observations about students' ability to identify the unit over the course of this Investigation.

Professional Development

⑤ **Dialogue Box:** *Break the Train,* p. 153

⑦ **Teacher Note:** What's the Unit?, p. 152

ONGOING ASSESSMENT: Observing Students at Work

Students construct linear repeating patterns and then break them down into units.

- **Are students able to identify the unit of the pattern?** Are they able to break apart the pattern train into units?
- **Can students reconstruct the pattern train once they have broken it apart?**

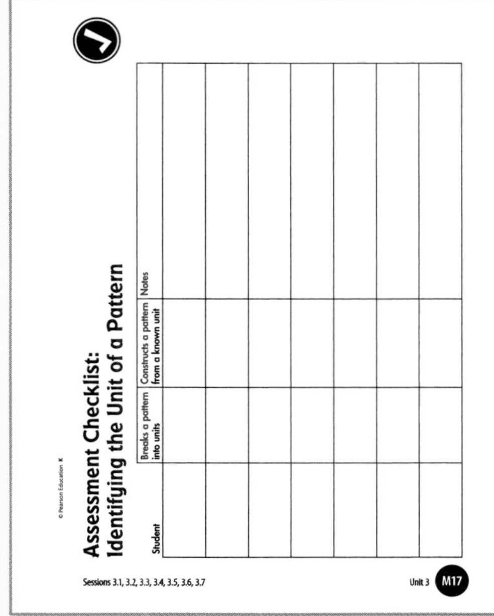

Assessment Checklist: Identifying the Unit of a Pattern

Student	Breaks a pattern into units	Constructs a pattern from a known unit	Notes

Sessions 3.1, 3.2, 3.3, 3.4, 3.5, 3.6, 3.7 Unit 3 M17

▲ Resource Masters, M17

DISCUSSION

Recording *Break the Train*

Math Focus Points for Discussion

- Counting the number of units in a repeating pattern
- Identifying the unit of a repeating pattern

Today when you played *Break the Train,* you broke your partner's train down into cars and then you put it together again. I am going to show you how you can record your cube train pattern on paper, record how you broke your train into cars, and record how many cars are in your train.

Show students *Student Activity Book* page 22.

Then show them the cube train pattern you made before.

Earlier, I made this cube train. The first thing this sheet says is that I should color in my cube train pattern.

Ask a student to tell you the colors in the cube train pattern as you color them on the sheet. Point out that your train is 12 cubes long and there are 12 squares to color in. Tell students they should color in their patterns before their partners break their trains.

Then, ask the students to help you break the train into cars.

Where should we break the train to make the first car? . . . After this first [red] cube? . . . After this [green] cube? . . . So, the cars in this train are one [red] cube and one [green] cube? Is that right?

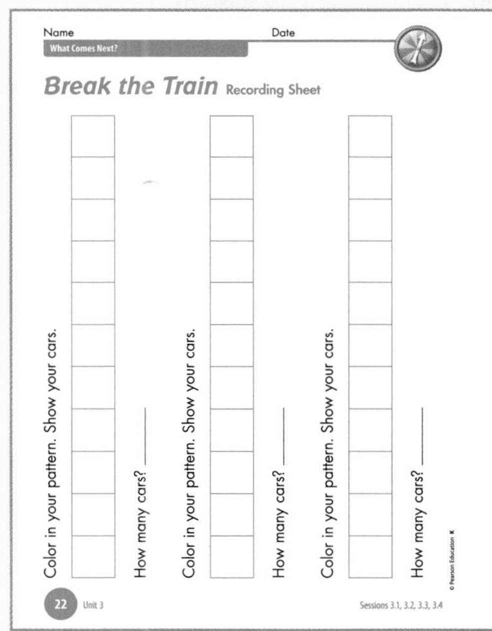

Name Date

What Comes Next?

Break the Train Recording Sheet

Color in your pattern. Show your cars.

How many cars? ____

Color in your pattern. Show your cars.

How many cars? ____

Color in your pattern. Show your cars.

How many cars? ____

22 Unit 3 Sessions 3.1, 3.2, 3.3, 3.4

▲ Student Activity Book, p. 22; Resource Masters, M18

Then, show them how to draw lines to indicate where each car ends.

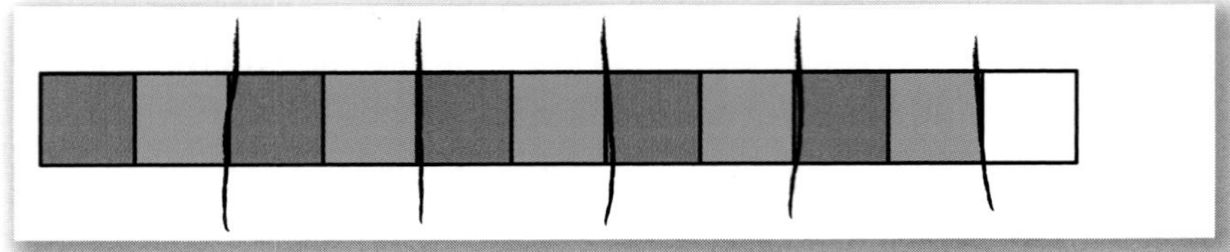

I am going to show where the cars are by drawing a big line between this [green] cube and this [red] cube. . . . Where does the next car end? . . . I am going to draw a big line there as well.

Continue drawing thick lines to mark the end of one unit and the beginning of another unit for the whole pattern you have drawn on the recording page. Then ask students to count the number of units.

How many cars are in this train?

First, count the number of cars you marked. Then, check by counting the number of cars the students made by breaking the train. Show students where to record the number of cars.

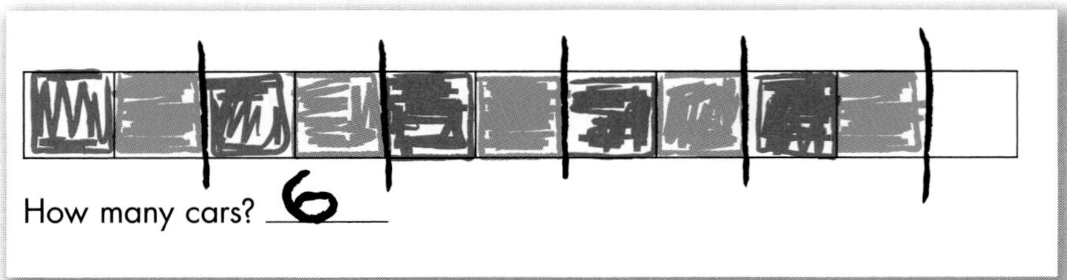

Sample Student Work

Choose another cube train pattern a student created and go through the same steps to record the pattern, the cars, and the number of cars.

Explain to the students that when they play *Break the Train* in Math Workshop, they will record their work on *Student Activity Book* page 22.

SESSION FOLLOW-UP
Practice

Student Math Handbook Flip Chart: Use the *Student Math Handbook Flip Chart* page 43 to reinforce concepts from today's session. See pages 165–166 in the back of this unit.

Recording Break the Train

Math Focus Points

- Counting, creating, and representing quantities
- Identifying the unit of a repeating pattern
- Counting the number of units in a repeating pattern

Today's Plan		Materials
1 ACTIVITY **Reintroducing *Break the Train*: Recording**	5 MIN CLASS	• *Student Activity Book,* p. 22 • Connecting cubes; crayons
2 MATH WORKSHOP **Identifying the Unit and Counting** 2A *Break the Train*: Recording 2B Counting Jar 2C *Add On:* Cubes, Pattern Blocks, and Two-Color Counters 2D Arrow Patterns	15–30 MIN	2A • *Student Activity Book,* p. 22 • M18 • Materials from Session 3.1, p. 114; crayons 2B • Counting Jar* • Materials for the Counting Jar (as you have set it up) 2C • Materials from Session 2.10, p. 103 2D • Materials from Session 2.8, p. 95
3 DISCUSSION **What's the Unit?**	10 MIN CLASS	
4 SESSION FOLLOW-UP **Practice**		• *Student Math Handbook Flip Chart,* p. 43

*See *Materials to Prepare,* p. 111.

Classroom Routines

Patterns on the Pocket Chart **Arrange an ABB repeating pattern on the pocket chart using ten Arrow Cards (down, up, up). Follow the basic *Patterns* activity. Students point in the direction they think is under each Question Mark Card.**

ACTIVITY

Reintroducing *Break the Train*: Recording

Construct an AB cube train pattern that is 12 cubes long. Then ask students to help you color in the pattern on the recording sheet.

Next, ask for volunteers to break the train into cars. Have each volunteer come up and break the train to make a car. Ask the other students whether they agree with where the train has been broken.

The students should then help you mark on the recording sheet with lines where each car ends and write down the total number of cars.

Tell students that they will record their own train on the student sheet even though they broke apart their partner's train.

MATH WORKSHOP

Identifying the Unit and Counting

Explain that the following four activities, one of which is the Counting Jar with a new set of materials, are available during Math Workshop. Remind students what each activity entails, what materials are required, and where they are located. This is the last day for Arrow Patterns.

2A *Break the Train:* Recording

Students construct cube train patterns using two colors and color the pattern they made on *Student Activity Book* page 22. They then break down the train their partners have made into units or "cars" and record the cars in their train and the numbers of cars in their train on the recording sheet. After they have checked each other's work, they put the trains back together again.

ONGOING ASSESSMENT: Observing Students at Work

Students construct linear repeating patterns and then break them down into units and record the pattern, units, and number of units.

- **Are students able to construct an AB pattern?** Are they constructing other patterns? (AAB, ABBA?)
- **Are students able to identify the unit of the pattern?** Are they able to break apart the pattern train into units?

- **Can students accurately record their patterns?** Can they show the units in the pattern? Do they correctly count the number of units?

- **Can students reconstruct the pattern train once they have broken it apart?**

DIFFERENTIATION: Supporting the Range of Learners

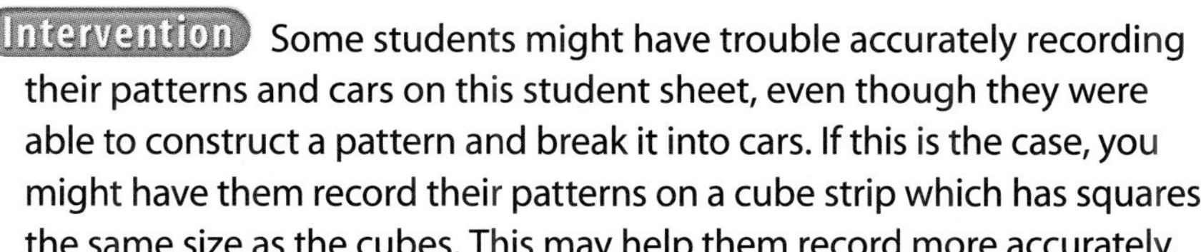

Intervention Some students might have trouble accurately recording their patterns and cars on this student sheet, even though they were able to construct a pattern and break it into cars. If this is the case, you might have them record their patterns on a cube strip which has squares the same size as the cubes. This may help them record more accurately.

2B Counting Jar

INDIVIDUALS

Students count the objects in the Counting Jar, record the amount counted, and make a set of the same size.

ONGOING ASSESSMENT: Observing Students at Work

Students count a set of objects, create an equivalent set, and record their work.

- **How do students count the objects in the jar?** Do they organize the objects in any way? Do they know the sequence of number names? Do they count each item once and only once? Do they double-check?

- **How do students create an equivalent set?** Do they think, "The Counting Jar had seven, so I need seven tiles. 1, 2, 3 . . ."? Do they recreate the Counting Jar set, matching them one-to-one? Do they double-check?

- **How do students represent the contents of the jar?** Do they use pictures or symbols? If so, do they draw one for each object or do they draw seven pictures because they counted seven objects? Do they use numbers? How do they figure out how to write a particular number?

- **Do students remember that the last Counting Jar had seven items in it as well?** Do they compare the two Counting Jars?

Professional Development

① **Teacher Note:** What's the Unit?, p. 152

2C *Add On:* Cubes, Pattern Blocks, and Two-Color Counters

PAIRS

For complete details about this activity, see Session 2.10, page 104.

2D Arrow Patterns

INDIVIDUALS

For complete details about this activity, see Session 2.8, page 96.

10 MIN CLASS

DISCUSSION

3 What's the Unit?

Math Focus Points for Discussion

- Identifying the unit of a repeating pattern

Construct an AAB pattern, that is 12 cubes long. Ask the whole class to say with you the colors of each cube in the pattern. Color in this pattern on the recording sheet.

We are going to break this train down into cars. Where does this pattern begin to repeat? Where is the first car?

Some students identify correctly the three cubes in each unit. Other students think the unit is still two cubes long. Other students think it is not possible to identify the unit or the car.①

Point to each cube at the beginning of the train. Ask, after pointing, whether the pattern has repeated yet.

The first cube in this train is [yellow]and then another [yellow]. Has the pattern repeated yet? Then there is a [blue]. Has it repeated yet? Why do you think so? And then a [yellow]? Has it repeated now? [Raul] says that this [yellow] is where it repeats. Why do you think so, [Raul]?

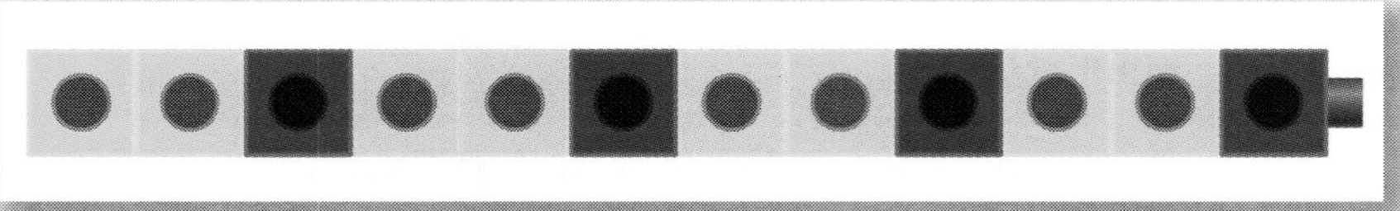

Once you have determined the first unit or car, ask the students to help you break the rest of the train. After you have broken the train into cars, go back over the train while saying each color aloud, and ask the class whether they agree on where you have broken the train into cars.

Then point out the pattern on the recording sheet and record the number of cars.

SESSION FOLLOW-UP

Practice

Student Math Handbook Flip Chart: Use the *Student Math Handbook Flip Chart* page 43 to reinforce concepts from today's session. See pages 165–166 in the back of this unit.

How Many Cars?

Math Focus Points

- Counting, creating, and representing quantities
- Identifying the unit of a repeating pattern
- Extending a repeating pattern by adding on units to the pattern

Today's Plan		Materials
1 ACTIVITY Introducing *How Many Cars?*	5–10 MIN, CLASS	• M19* • Connecting cubes; 1-to-6 number cube
2 MATH WORKSHOP What's the Unit? 2A *How Many Cars?* 2B *Break the Train:* Recording 2C Counting Jar 2D *Add On:* Cubes, Pattern Blocks, and Two-Color Counters	20–30 MIN	2A • Connecting cubes; Car Cards; 1-to-6 number cube 2B • Materials from Session 3.2, p. 119 2C • Materials from Session 3.2, p. 119 2D • Materials from Session 2.10, p. 103
3 DISCUSSION Checking In	5 MIN, CLASS	
4 SESSION FOLLOW-UP Practice		• *Student Math Handbook Flip Chart,* p. 43

*See *Materials to Prepare,* p. 111.

Classroom Routines

Calendar: What's Missing? **Remove two dates on the monthly calendar. Challenge students to tell you which cards are missing and how they know.**

1

ACTIVITY

Introducing *How Many Cars?*

Tell students you are going to show them another game using cube train patterns.

I am going to show you another game you can play today during Math Workshop. It is called *How Many Cars*? In this game, instead of breaking a cube train into cars, as you did in *Break the Train,* you are going to be making a cube train pattern by putting cars together.

Ask for a volunteer to play the game with you. Show students one set of the Car Cards that you created from Car Cards (M19). Put the cards face down and ask your partner to pick one.

First you pick a Car Card. The car card tells you what the cars in your train are going to be. [Mitchell] picked this card, it has a [blue] cube and a [yellow] cube on it. So the cars in our train are going to be [blue, yellow]. Now I am going to roll the number cube. The number cube tells us how many cars we need to make for our train.

Roll the number cube.

I rolled a [3]. So we are going to have [3] cars in our train. Our cars will be [blue, yellow], and there will be [3] cars in our train. Let's build our first car. What color cubes do we need?

Take out the two cubes you need and snap them together.

So far our train has one car. We are supposed to make a train with [three] cars. What can we do to make our train [three] cars of [blue, yellow]?

Some students suggest making three separate cars and then snapping them together. Others suggest adding on [blue, yellow] until you have the pattern three times.

Try out the methods students suggest. If students do not have any suggestions, demonstrate a method yourself.

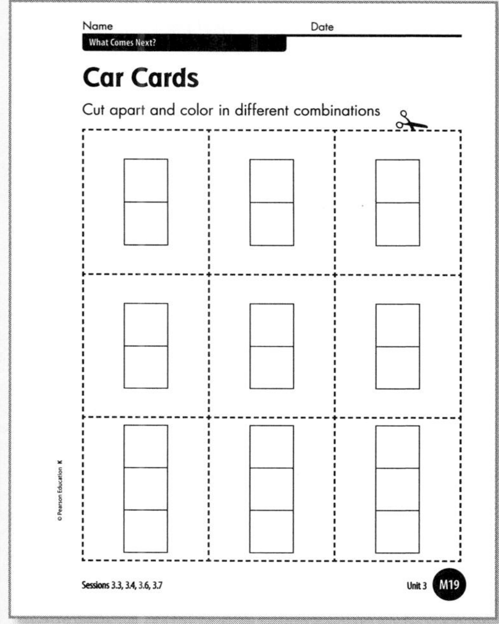
Name Date

What Comes Next?

Car Cards

Cut apart and color in different combinations

© Pearson Education K

Sessions 3.3, 3.4, 3.6, 3.7 Unit 3 M19

▲ Resource Masters, M19

Math Note

❶ **Number of Cars vs. Number of Cubes** Students may think that the number they roll on the number cube tells them the number of cubes they are supposed to put in their train, not the number of cars. Counting two cubes as one unit may be a difficult concept for some students. Help students count the number of cars on their trains so far.

A teacher and student play How Many Cars?

Now we have our cube train. Let's check our train to make sure we made it correctly. This card told us we needed to make all our cars [blue, yellow] and the number cube told us we needed [3] cars. Do we have [3] cars that are [blue, yellow]? How can we tell?

Some students suggest taking the train apart into cars, seeing whether they are [blue, yellow] and counting them. Others suggest counting them in the train. Try the methods they suggest.

Play another round of *How Many Cars?* with the students.

MATH WORKSHOP

What's the Unit?

20–30 MIN

Explain that the following four activities are available during Math Workshop. Remind students what each activity entails, what materials are required, and where they are located. This is the last day for the *Add On* activity.

2A How Many Cars?

PAIRS

Students play *How Many Cars*? in which they build cube train patterns from known units. They pick a Car Card, which shows the color of the cars in their train; roll a number cube, which tells the number of cars in their train; and then construct their cube train pattern.❶

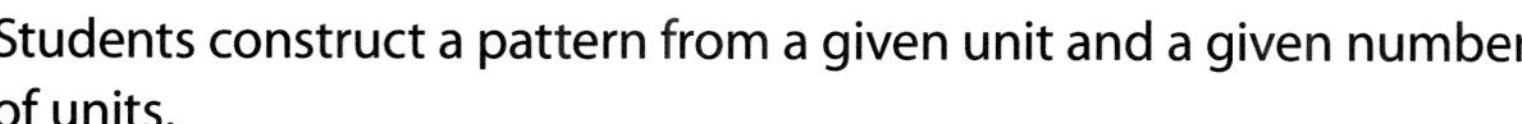

ONGOING ASSESSMENT: Observing Students at Work

Students construct a pattern from a given unit and a given number of units.

- **Can students correctly construct a pattern, given the unit and number of units?**
- **How do students construct the pattern?** Do they construct the units first, count them, and then snap them together? Do they add on to the train until they have the number of units indicated?

DIFFERENTIATION: Supporting the Range of Learners

Intervention Some students may need a reminder that the number on the cube tells them the number of cars.

This is one car. Can you make two cars? Can you make three cars?

Count the cars together and then ask the students to put them in a train. Then count the cars again.

2B *Break the Train*: Recording

PAIRS

For complete details about this activity, see Session 3.2, page 120.

DIFFERENTIATION: Supporting the Range of Learners

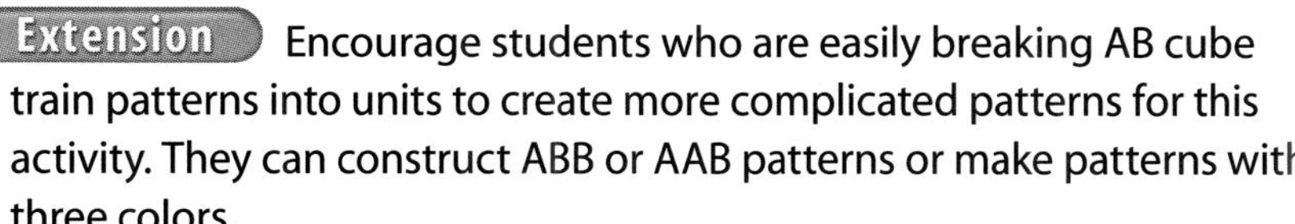

Extension Encourage students who are easily breaking AB cube train patterns into units to create more complicated patterns for this activity. They can construct ABB or AAB patterns or make patterns with three colors.

2C Counting Jar

INDIVIDUALS

For complete details about this activity, see Session 3.2, page 121.

2D *Add On:* Cubes, Pattern Blocks, and Two-Color Counters

PAIRS

For complete details about this activity, see Session 2.10, page 104.

DISCUSSION

Checking In

Take this opportunity to discuss any issues that you noticed while observing students at work. The topic might be mathematical (e.g., strategies for identifying the unit of a non-AB pattern) or logistical (e.g., the steps for the *How Many Cars?* game) in nature, or it may relate to a management issue (e.g., working together on *How Many Cars?*) that arose during the session.

Other alternatives include checking with students about which activities they have been choosing (e.g., "Thumbs up if you worked on *Break the Train*. Thumbs up if you worked on *How Many Cars?*"), asking everyone to hold up a piece of work, or encouraging students to raise a question or make a comment about that day's math class.

SESSION FOLLOW-UP

Practice

Student Math Handbook Flip Chart: Use the *Student Math Handbook Flip Chart* page 43 to reinforce concepts of this unit's content. See pages 165–166 in the back of this unit.

Break the Train with Other Materials

Math Focus Points

- Counting, creating, and representing quantities
- Identifying the unit of a repeating pattern
- Extending a repeating pattern by adding on units to the pattern

Vocabulary

unit

Today's Plan			Materials
1 ACTIVITY **Introducing *Break the Train* with Other Materials**	5–10 MIN	CLASS	• Pattern blocks; Arrow Cards; toothpicks
2 MATH WORKSHOP **Identifying the Unit with New Materials** 2A *Break the Train* with Other Materials 2B *How Many Cars?* 2C *Break the Train*: Recording 2D Counting Jar	15–25 MIN		2A • Pattern blocks; two-color counters; Arrow Cards; toothpicks 2B • Materials from Session 3.3, p. 124 2C • Materials from Session 3.2, p. 119 2D • Materials from Session 3.2, p. 119
3 DISCUSSION **Counting Jar**	10 MIN	CLASS	• Materials for Counting Jar (from Math Workshop)
4 SESSION FOLLOW-UP **Practice**			• *Student Activity Book,* p. 23

Classroom Routines

Attendance: Comparing Groups Count around the circle as usual and then count the number of boys and the number of girls present in class. Ask students whether there are more boys or girls. Have the boys make a line and the girls make a line opposite them. Count the number of students in each line, and ask again whether there are more boys or girls. Challenge students to figure out how many more and then discuss their strategies.

ACTIVITY

1 Introducing *Break the Train* with Other Materials

Make an AB pattern with pattern blocks.

You have been playing *Break the Train* with cubes. You can also play *Break the Train* with other materials. When you played *Break the Train* with cube trains, you broke your trains into cars. The car is the part of your pattern that repeats over and over again. Mathematicians call the part of the pattern that repeats the unit. So you have been breaking your patterns into units.

Look at the pattern you made with pattern blocks. What is the car or unit of your pattern?

What is the part that repeats over and over in this pattern? Where does the first car or unit end?

Ask a volunteer to point out the first unit.

I am going to mark the cars in this train with toothpicks in the same way you marked the cars on your *Break the Train* Recording Sheet with lines.

Place a toothpick between the first and second car. Ask students to point out where each car is, and put a toothpick at the end of each car.

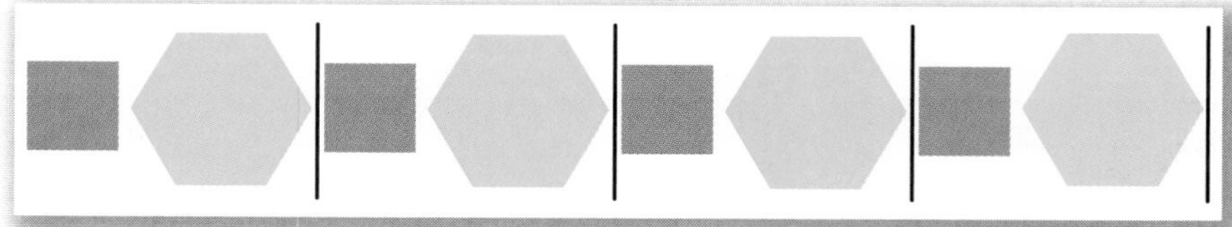

What is the car or unit in this pattern? How many units are in this pattern?

Make an AAB pattern with Arrow Cards (M16). Ask students to help you mark the units using toothpicks. Then ask:

What is the car or unit in this pattern? How many units are in this pattern?

Tell students that they can play *Break the Train* with pattern blocks or Arrow Cards. Remind them that in *Break the Train* they construct the pattern and their partners break the pattern into cars or units. They can continue to play the original *Break the Train* and record their work on *Student Activity Book* page 22 or on *Break the Train* Recording Sheet (M18). They will not be recording *Break the Train* with other materials.

15–25 MIN

MATH WORKSHOP

Identifying the Unit with New Materials

Explain that the following four activities are available during Math Workshop. Remind students what each activity entails, what materials are required, and where they are located. Students need to do the Counting Jar activity by the end of this Math Workshop.

PAIRS

2A *Break the Train* with Other Materials

Students construct patterns using pattern blocks, two-color counters, or Arrow Cards. They then break the patterns their partners have made into units or cars by marking the units with toothpicks.

ONGOING ASSESSMENT: Observing Students at Work

Students construct linear repeating patterns and then break them down into units.

- **What type of two-element patterns are students constructing?** (AB, AAB, ABBA?)
- **Are students able to identify the unit of the pattern?** Are they able to break the pattern train into units?
- **Can students reconstruct their pattern once they have broken it apart?**

PAIRS

2B *How Many Cars?*

For complete details about this activity, see Session 3.3, page 125.

DIFFERENTIATION: Supporting the Range of Learners

Extension You can create car cards that are ABC, AAB, or ABB units, and ask students who are easily making AB patterns to play with these cards.

PAIRS

2C *Break the Train:* Recording

For complete details about this activity, see Session 3.2, page 120.

2D Counting Jar

INDIVIDUALS

For complete details about this activity, see Session 3.2, page 121.

10 MIN CLASS

DISCUSSION

3 Counting Jar

Math Focus Points for Discussion

- Counting, creating, and representing quantities

Display the Counting Jar poster, with students' representations on it, so that all of the students can see it. If students kept records in individual Counting Jar booklets, ask them to bring them to the discussion, open to that page.

Ask students how many objects they found in the Counting Jar. Have several students count the objects, and then count them together as a class to check.

If no one remarks that the same quantity of objects was in the jar this time as the last time they worked on the Counting Jar (which they discussed in Session 2.1), ask students to compare the two counting jars.

What was in the Counting Jar the last time you worked on it? How many cubes were there? What do you notice about the Counting Jar this time compared with last time?

Some students notice that there were [7] items in the jar last time and [7] items in the jar this time, but that they were different items. Some are surprised that it was the same quantity because one set of items was a lot bigger than the other. If no one brings this up introduce it yourself.

Put out [7] cubes.

There were [7] cubes last time and [7] [tennis balls] this time. How is that possible? The [7] [tennis balls] filled the jar up to the very top, and the [7] cubes were just a little bit in the bottom of the jar.

Some students explain that the [tennis balls] are a lot bigger so they take up more room. Other students are not troubled by the fact that the same quantity looked different because they may not yet have a sense that a quantity should be constant.

How could we check that they are the same amount?

Some students suggest counting each set and seeing whether there are [seven] of each. Others suggest lining them up next to each other in order to match one [tennis ball] to each cube. Do whatever methods they suggest.

Then, look together at a few of the student equivalent sets and check that there are [7] objects in each set.

Finally, have a few students share how they represented what and how many were in the Counting Jar.

SESSION FOLLOW-UP

Practice

Practice: For reinforcement of this unit's content, have students complete *Student Activity Book* page 23.

Name Date

What Comes Next? Practice

What Comes Next?

NOTE Students practice extending repeating patterns.

Draw what comes next if the pattern continues.

© Pearson Education K

Session 3.4 Unit 3 23

▲ Student Activity Book, p. 23

SESSION 3.5

12 Chips

Math Focus Points

- Constructing a variety of patterns using the same elements
- Identifying the unit of a repeating pattern
- Counting the number of units in a repeating pattern

Today's Plan			Materials
1 ACTIVITY **Introducing 12 Chips**	10 MIN	CLASS	• *Student Activity Book,* p. 24 • Two-color counters; red and yellow paper circles
2 ACTIVITY **12 Chips**	10–25 MIN	INDIVIDUALS	• M20* • Materials from Activity 1
3 DISCUSSION **A Variety of Patterns for 12 Chips**	10 MIN	CLASS	• *Student Activity Book,* p. 24 • Chart paper
4 SESSION FOLLOW-UP **Practice**	5 MIN	CLASS	• *Student Math Handbook Flip Chart,* p. 43

*See *Materials to Prepare,* p. 113.

Classroom Routines

Today's Question: Would you rather jump in a pile of leaves or play in the snow?

On chart paper, create a vertical two-column table titled, "Would you rather jump in a pile of leaves or play in the snow?" with the column label "Leaves" written at the bottom of one column and "Snow" written at the bottom of the other column. Students respond by writing their names above the appropriate heading. Count the responses as a class and discuss what the results of the survey tell you. Continue to ask about and experiment with different ways to organize the data so that it is easier to tell which group has more.

ACTIVITY 1
Introducing 12 Chips

Gather students in a circle on the floor as you demonstrate this activity.

Show the set of 12 two-color counters that you have prepared. Ask students to suggest a possible pattern using the two colors. Then, build that pattern using all 12 counters. Flip over the counters as needed.

Say the colors of the counters in the pattern aloud as a class, and ask students to confirm that it is a pattern. Then, ask them to identify the unit of the pattern.

Show students *Student Activity Book* page 24. Read the directions aloud.

This is a sheet to record your patterns on. It is a lot like the sheet for *Break the Train* with cubes. First, we are going to record our pattern by coloring in the circles. Can you tell me what color to color each circle?

Color in the pattern, following students' directions.

Now we need to show the units of our pattern by drawing lines between the units. What is the unit of this pattern? What part of the pattern repeats? Where should I draw a line?

Mark off all of the units in the pattern you constructed.

Now let's count how many units there are in our pattern.

Count the units and write down the quantity on the appropriate line.

Do you think we can make a different pattern using these 12 two-color counters? We just made a [red–yellow–red–yellow] pattern. Who has an idea for a different pattern?

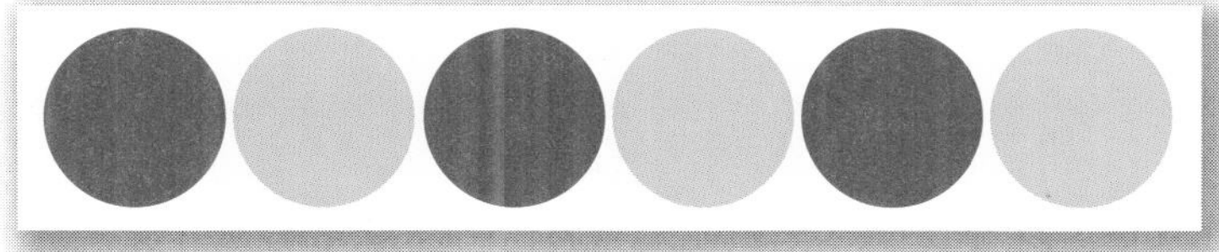

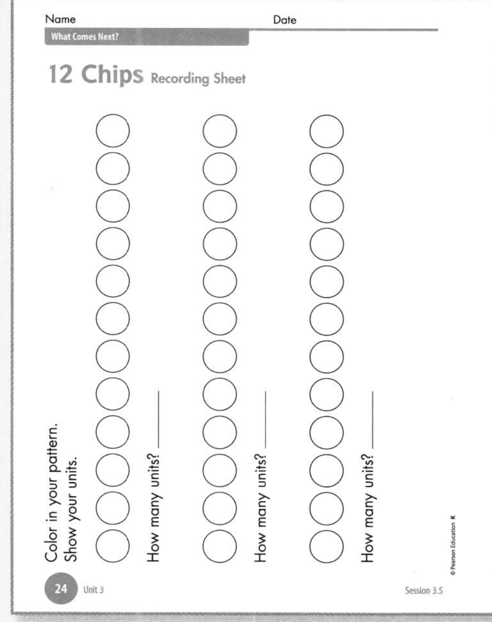

Name Date

What Comes Next?

12 Chips Recording Sheet

Color in your pattern.
Show your units.

How many units? ______

How many units? ______

How many units? ______

24 Unit 3 Session 3.5

© Pearson Education K

▲ Student Activity Book, p. 24; Resource Masters, M20

Collect possible ideas and demonstrate one of the patterns. Say the colors of the pattern aloud together as a class. Then, record the pattern, mark the units, and count the number of units.

We have made two different patterns using these 12 counters. Do you think there are other patterns we could make with these 12 counters?

Explain that in this activity students will look for different ways they can make patterns using a set of 12 counters. Emphasize that each arrangement of the counters they record must be a pattern.

ACTIVITY 2

12 Chips

Students construct a variety of patterns using 12 two-color counters. They record their patterns, identify the units, and count the number of units in their patterns.[1]

ONGOING ASSESSMENT: Observing Students at Work

Students construct a variety of patterns with only two elements. They identify the unit in each of their patterns and count the number of units in their pattern.

- **Are students able to make a variety of patterns using two colors (ABB, AAB, AABB, AAAB), or do they make only an AB pattern?**
- **Are students able to record their patterns accurately?** Are they able to identify the unit in each pattern? Do they accurately count the units?
- **Do students use their recording sheet to compare different patterns made with two colors?**

DIFFERENTIATION: Supporting the Range of Learners

Intervention Some students may make only AB patterns. If students are having difficulty with more complex patterns, start a more complex pattern such as ABB and ask them to extend it.

Math Note

1 **Repeating the Same Pattern** Some students may repeat a pattern they constructed or even repeat the same one or two patterns over and over again. Ask these students to say the colors of each of their patterns in order, and then ask them whether they think any of the patterns are the same. Some students identify patterns that are the same, and others don't. If students are constructing only AB patterns, see Supporting the Range of Learners for ways to support them in constructing other patterns.

3 DISCUSSION

A Variety of Patterns for 12 Chips

Math Focus Points for Discussion

- Constructing a variety of patterns using the same elements

Students bring the patterns they have recorded so far for 12 Chips to this discussion.

On a piece of chart paper, draw the two patterns you constructed when you introduced 12 Chips.

These are the two patterns we made when we first talked about the 12 Chips activity. When you were working on 12 Chips, I noticed that you came up with some other patterns as well. Who came up with another pattern that is not this one or this one?

Ask the student who suggests another pattern to say the colors used in the pattern he or she created. Show it with the two-color counters.

Is this pattern different from the patterns we already have here? How is it different?

If everyone agrees that it is a different pattern, record it on the chart paper. If not, make a check mark next to the pattern it copies and do not record it.

Ask for another suggestion, and show the pattern with two-color counters. Ask the same questions. If everyone agrees that it is a different pattern, record it on the chart paper. If not, make a check mark next to the pattern it copies and do not record it.

Record a number of patterns on the chart paper.

During Math Workshop tomorrow, one of the activities you can do is 12 Chips. If you do this activity, you can make one of these patterns or you can see whether you can find another pattern that we didn't make yet.

SESSION FOLLOW-UP

Practice

Student Math Handbook Flip Chart: Use the *Student Math Handbook Flip Chart* page 43 to reinforce this unit's content. See pages 165–166 in the back of this unit.

End-of-Unit Assessment and Comparing Patterns

Math Focus Points

- Identifying the unit of a repeating pattern
- Extending a repeating pattern by adding on units to the pattern
- Comparing different kinds of patterns

Today's Plan		Materials
1 DISCUSSION **Units in the Pocket Chart**	5–10 MIN CLASS	• Pocket 100 chart; pattern blocks; Question Mark Cards
2 MATH WORKSHOP **Assessment Workshop** 2A End-of-Unit Assessments 2B 12 Chips 2C *Break the Train* with Other Materials 2D *How Many Cars?*	15–25 MIN	2A • Connecting cubes; prepared cube trains for assessment* 2B • Materials from Session 3.5, p. 134 2C • Materials from Session 3.4, p. 129 2D • Materials from Session 3.3, p. 124
3 DISCUSSION **Comparing Patterns**	10 MIN CLASS	• Prepared cube trains for discussion*
4 SESSION FOLLOW-UP **Practice**		• *Student Activity Book,* p. 25

*See *Materials to Prepare,* p. 113.

Classroom Routines

Patterns on the Pocket Chart **Arrange an ABB repeating pattern on the pocket chart using ten pattern blocks (blue rhombus, red trapezoid, red trapezoid). Follow the basic *Patterns* activity. Students hold up the block they think is under each Question Mark Card.**

DISCUSSION

Units in the Pocket Chart

5–10 MIN CLASS

Math Focus Points for Discussion

- Extending a repeating pattern by adding on units to the pattern

Secretly make the following pattern in the pocket chart: green triangle, yellow hexagon, orange square, green triangle, yellow hexagon, orange square, and so on. Cover all but the first three pattern blocks with Question Mark cards. Point out the first three pattern blocks, the only ones that are revealed in the pattern you made.

Here is the unit of the pattern I made: [green triangle, yellow hexagon, orange square]. What would come next in this pattern if we wanted to repeat this unit over and over again? . . . Why do you think that would be the next pattern block?

Try students' suggestions, and then ask a student to say the names of the pattern blocks in the pattern so far. Then, ask them what they think will come next in the pattern. Continue until you have filled a whole line in the pocket chart.

Secretly make another pattern on the next line of the pocket chart. For example, try the following: trapezoid, trapezoid, triangle, trapezoid, trapezoid, triangle, and so on. Cover all but the first unit of the pattern (trapezoid, trapezoid, triangle). Point out the unit that is uncovered for the pattern you have made on the next line of the pocket chart. Follow the same procedure. If you have time, do another one or two patterns.

2 MATH WORKSHOP

Assessment Workshop

15–25 MIN

Explain that the following three activities are available during Math Workshop: 12 Chips, *Break the Train* with Other Materials, and *How Many Cars?* Remind students what each activity entails, what materials are required, and where they are located. Explain that while others are at work on these activities, you will be meeting with students individually.[1]

2A End-of-Unit Assessments

INDIVIDUALS

While students are working, meet individually with those you have identified as not yet meeting one or more of the benchmarks.[2]

Teaching Notes

[1] **Classroom Management** During this Math Workshop and the next, you will be meeting with individual students. Therefore, students will need to work independently on other activities. Review any policies you have about such work time. For example, some teachers have an "ask three before me" rule, which requires that students ask three peers before coming to the teacher with a question.

[2] **Preparing for End-of-Unit Assessment** Before Session 3.6, gather the assessment checklists you have filled in over the course of this unit: Assessment Checklist: Repeating Patterns (M3) and Assessment Checklist: Identifying the Unit in a Pattern (M17). For each benchmark, look over your notes and sort students into three categories: those who have clearly met the benchmark, those who have not yet met the benchmark, and those you have questions about. You will be meeting with the students in the latter two categories over the course of Sessions 3.6 and 3.7. You do not need to meet with students who your notes show can consistently meet the benchmarks of the unit. Make a list of students you need to meet with that specifies which tasks you need to do with each student.

For Benchmark 1, identify students who are having difficulty copying, constructing, or extending simple repeating patterns. Ask these students to construct a cube train pattern and then to describe their pattern. Then, ask them to extend their pattern three or four cubes more (they can extend it one cube at a time). If they are able to construct a pattern and extend it, they meet the benchmark.

If they are not able to construct a pattern and extend it, ask them to copy one of the AB cube train patterns you constructed, describe it, and extend it. This will allow you to find out whether they are able to copy and extend a pattern made by someone else, even if they cannot construct their own.

If they are not able to extend your pattern, show them four of the cube trains you prepared: one AB pattern, one ABC pattern, and two cube trains that have assorted colors in a non-repeating pattern. Ask them to identify which are patterns and which are not. This will allow you to find out whether they can discriminate between a pattern and a non-pattern, even if they cannot copy and extend a pattern.

For Benchmark 2, identify students who are having difficulty identifying the unit of a repeating pattern. Give these students one of the AB cube train patterns you constructed. Ask the students to break the cube train into cars or units. If the students can break the cube train pattern into units, they meet the benchmark.

If students are not able to break the cube train you constructed into units, ask them to construct their own cube train pattern and break it into cars or units. If they are able to break it into units, you will know that they can identify the unit in their own train, even if they cannot identify the unit in a cube train constructed by someone else.

For complete details about this activity, see Session 3.5, pages 135–136.

2C *Break the Train* with Other Materials

For complete details about this activity, See Session 3.4, page 130.

2D *How Many Cars?*

For complete details about this activity, See Session 3.3, page 125.

3 DISCUSSION

Comparing Patterns

Math Focus Points for Discussion

- Comparing different kinds of patterns

Place the five cube trains you made for discussion ahead of time where students can see them.

I made five cube trains. Look carefully at each cube train. What do you notice about each?

Some students notice that they are all different. Others point out that one is not a pattern. Still others notice similarities between some of the cube trains.

Are all of these cube train patterns? How can you tell?

Students might say:

"That one isn't a pattern. You can't figure out what goes next. It's all different colors."

"These are patterns because they repeat over and over."

A few students may say that the ABB pattern is not a pattern because it doesn't alternate colors. Others may say it is a pattern because it a has a unit or car that can repeat.

Talk briefly about what they think would come next in each cube train.

Put aside the cube train you determine is not a pattern, and ask students to compare the other cube trains.

How would you describe these patterns? How are these patterns the same? How are they different?

Name Date

What Comes Next? Practice

A Pattern of Buttons

NOTE Students make a repeating pattern.

Jae decorated a picture frame with buttons. He made a pattern.

1. Some buttons are missing. Draw the missing buttons. Follow the pattern.
2. How many buttons did Jae use?

© Pearson Education K

Session 3.6 Unit 3 25

▲ Student Activity Book, p. 25

Students might say:

"These two are kind of the same because they go back and forth with colors. This one goes red, blue, red, blue. This one goes yellow, green, yellow, green."

"These two are kind of the same. They have the same colors."

Students identify that the trains are different because the colors or the patterns are different.

I wonder how many cars are in each of these train patterns?

Ask for volunteers to break each train into units. After they have done this, ask the other students to confirm that they have been broken correctly. Then count the number of cars in each train.

Hmm . . . some of these trains have [six] cars and some have [four] cars. I wonder why that is?

Some students point out that some of the trains have cars that are three cubes and some have cars that are two cubes. Others do not see the correspondence between the number of cubes in a car and the number of cars.

4 SESSION FOLLOW-UP
Practice

Practice: For enrichment, have students complete *Student Activity Book* page 25.

End-of-Unit Assessment and the Pattern Display

Math Focus Points

- Identifying the unit of a repeating pattern
- Counting the number of units in a repeating pattern
- Extending a repeating pattern by adding on units to the pattern
- Comparing different kinds of patterns

Today's Plan		Materials
1 DISCUSSION **Can You Do What I Do?**	5–10 MIN CLASS	
2 MATH WORKSHOP **Assessment Workshop** 2A End-of-Unit Assessments 2B 12 Chips 2C *Break the Train* with Other Materials 2D *How Many Cars?*	15–25 MIN	2A • Materials from Session 3.6, p. 138 2B • Materials from Session 3.5, p. 134 2C • Materials from Session 3.4, p. 129 2D • Materials from Session 3.3, p. 124
3 DISCUSSION **The Pattern Display**	10 MIN CLASS	• The Pattern Display from Sessions 2.1–3.7
4 SESSION FOLLOW-UP **Practice**		• *Student Math Handbook Flip Chart*, pp. 39, 43

Classroom Routines

Calendar: How Many Days . . . ? **Students use the calendar to determine how many days there are until a class event or holiday this month. Discuss students' strategies for determining the number of days.**

DISCUSSION

Can You Do What I Do?

Math Focus Points for Discussion

- Identifying the unit of a repeating pattern

Begin with a two-step pattern made of hand gestures such as: *clap your hands, tap your shoulders.* Ask students to join in and do the actions with you.

Continue until all students are moving with you. Then, as before, ask:

How did you know what to do? How did you know what came next? How would you describe what we were doing to someone else?

After students have described the pattern and how they knew what came next, ask them to identify the unit of this pattern.

What is the unit of the pattern we have been making? What have we been repeating over and over?

Ask some students to show what they think the unit is. Ask other students whether they agree. After students show the unit with their bodies, begin repeating the unit to make a pattern, and decide together whether it is the pattern you were making before.

Ask a student to make a pattern with hand gestures and follow the same steps: describe it and then identify the unit.

If you have time, follow up with one more pattern, this time with one that is ABB, ABC, or AAB.

MATH WORKSHOP

Assessment Workshop

Explain that the following activities are available during Math Workshop. Remind students what each activity entails, what materials are required, and where they are located. Remind students that while others are at work on these activities, you will be meeting with students individually.

For complete details about this activity, See Session 3.6, pages 139–140.

As you do the End-of-Unit Assessment interviews, you may come across students who do not yet meet one or both of the benchmarks. Watch closely as these students complete the assessment tasks to figure out, as specifically as you can, what it is these students are struggling with. For example, does the student need more practice constructing a pattern, extending his or her own or another person's pattern, or even simply distinguishing between a pattern, and a non-pattern? With such specific information, you can plan the next steps to match students' needs, from meeting with them one-on-one or working with a small group to assigning particular activities during Math Workshop.

2B 12 Chips

INDIVIDUALS

For complete details about this activity, See Session 3.5, pages 135–136.

2C *Break the Train* with Other Materials

PAIRS

For complete details about this activity, See Session 3.4, page 130.

2D *How Many Cars?*

PAIRS

For complete details about this activity, See Session 3.3, page 125.

3 DISCUSSION
The Pattern Display

10 MIN CLASS

Math Focus Points for Discussion

- Comparing different kinds of patterns

If the Pattern Display is not in an area where you usually have discussions, gather students around the Pattern Display or bring it to where you have discussions.

Ask students what they notice about the patterns in the display.

Over the last few weeks we have been collecting patterns. Some of these patterns you brought from home, some of them I brought in, and some you made yourselves. What do you notice about these patterns? Are there any that particularly interest you? Are there any that seem similar or very different?

DIFFERENTIATION: Supporting the Range of Learners

ELL You may want to preview the Pattern Display with a small group of English Language Learners so they can prepare their thoughts for the whole class discussion. If English Language Learners have trouble expressing their ideas, you can help them put their thoughts into words.

Kiyo, you pointed to these two patterns. What do you notice about them? Are they similar or different? Yes, these two patterns are very similar. What makes them similar? Do they use the same colors or the same shapes?

Students share what they notice about the patterns—which they find interesting or think are similar or different. Some students disagree over whether some of the arrangements are patterns or not. Ask them to explain why they think one is a pattern or not a pattern, and ask them to think about what makes something a pattern.

Ask students to describe a few of the patterns and, if possible, say what they think might come next in the patterns if they continued.

After looking carefully at a few of the patterns, talk again about the variety of patterns in this collection.

During the last few weeks, we have been making patterns from pattern blocks, cubes, two-color counters, arrows, and other things. There are many different kinds of patterns you can find in our classroom, in our school, and in our neighborhood. There are patterns that cover a piece of cloth or a border in a book. There are patterns on buildings and in nature. There are patterns to look for when you work with numbers and with shapes. You will have many more chances to work with patterns in other grades as well.

SESSION FOLLOW-UP

Practice

Student Math Handbook Flip Chart: Use the *Student Math Handbook Flip Chart* pages 39 and 43 to reinforce concepts from today's session. See pages 165–166 in the back of this unit.

Professional Development

UNIT 3

What Comes Next?

Teacher Notes

In Part 6 of *Implementing Investigations in Kindergarten,* you will find a set of Teacher Notes that addresses topics and issues applicable to the curriculum as a whole rather than to specific curriculum units. They include the following:

Computational Fluency and Place Value

Computation Algorithms and Methods

Representations and Contexts for Mathematical Work

Foundations of Algebra in the Elementary Grades

Discussing Mathematical Ideas

Racial and Linguistic Diversity in the Classroom: Raising Questions About What Equity in the Math Classroom Means Today

Dialogue Boxes

Repeating Patterns

Mathematics has been called "the science of patterns," for it is often used as a language to describe and determine numerical or geometric regularities. In this unit, students are learning to think about regularity and repetition through building and analyzing repeating color, shape, and movement patterns.

Determining the Basic Unit

All of the patterns students study in this unit, and probably all or most of the patterns they construct, are built by repeating a basic unit—the segment of the pattern that is repeated over and over. The simplest repeating pattern is constructed by repeating a unit that has two different elements that alternate, such as a border of tiles in a black-white-black-white sequence around the edge of a bathtub. A repeating pattern with two elements that alternate can be referred to as an AB pattern. In this case the A designates a black tile and the B designates a white tile:

In this tile pattern, the unit consists of a black tile followed by a white tile:

In this unit, students will study more complicated patterns such as the movement pattern clap–slap knees–slap knees–clap slap–slap. The unit *clap–slap knees–slap knees* repeats to make the pattern. A cube train made up of the cubes red–yellow–yellow–red–yellow–yellow has *red–yellow–yellow* as its unit. We can call these patterns ABB patterns because their unit consists of two elements, the first of which occurs once (A) and the second of which occurs twice (BB):

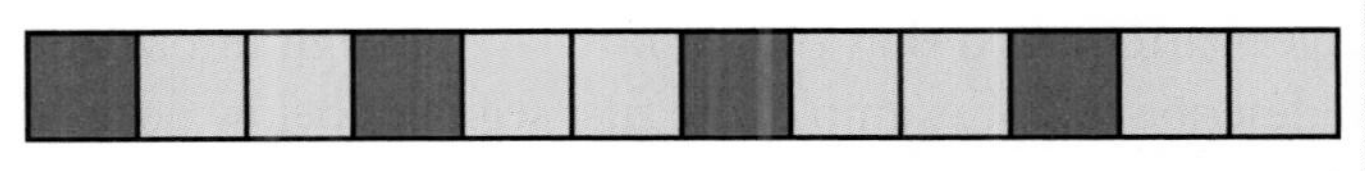

Although adults easily recognize that a red–green–red–green repeating pattern and a blue–yellow–blue–yellow repeating pattern are both AB patterns, to many kindergarteners these two patterns are completely different because they are different colors. Students need many opportunities to describe the patterns they are studying and constructing in ways that make sense to them and in ways that will help them extend the patterns. Although students will have some opportunities to compare patterns in this unit, generalizing patterns will be the focus of pattern work in later grades.

Determining the Next Element

One of the questions students investigate about repeating patterns is "What comes next?" As your students construct and discuss a variety of repeating patterns, most of them will extend a repeating pattern by thinking about "what comes after what." For example, for the cube sequence yellow–red–yellow–red–yellow–red, students will not necessarily think about the pattern as being made from the unit yellow–red. Rather, they will think of the pattern as "red comes after yellow; yellow comes after red." They think about the action of building a sequence in order to understand the pattern. For kindergarteners, this is an appropriate entry into work with repeating patterns. But as they work on more complex patterns, simply following the sequence in order to build a pattern becomes more difficult. You will notice some differences in the students' descriptions, depending on whether they are beginning to see the units in a pattern or are following the sequence, cube by cube, as in **Dialogue Box:** I Think It's Green, page 161.

Throughout this unit, students are asked to determine what comes later in the patterns they are considering. It is important to remember that unless you are told that you have enough information to analyze the structure and identify the unit of a repeating pattern, it is always possible that the part of the pattern that can be seen is part of a larger pattern, and that you do not have enough information to describe it. For example, the first segment below does not look like a repeating pattern by itself, but it could be part of a repeating pattern such as the one below it:

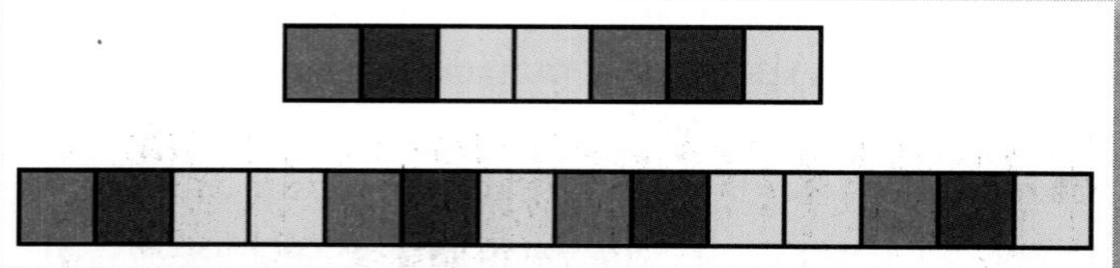

This idea can come up as students play *What Comes Next?* a game in which they determine the next elements in a repeating pattern. In **Dialogue Box:** A "Harder" Pattern, page 163, Corey moves beyond an AB repeating pattern and tries to make a harder one for her partner, Manuel. But when she reveals only two elements of her three-part pattern, she does not give her partner the chance to see the whole unit. Manuel bases his answer on his prior experience with two-part (AB) patterns. Once he sees the next piece, he is confused because it does not match his scheme for how patterns repeat.

After being provided with more information, Manuel is able to adjust his thinking and successfully determine the remaining hidden elements of the pattern. Through this interaction, the teacher is able to focus attention on several issues, including clearly identifying the unit that repeats and having enough information in order to accurately determine what comes next.

This unit may be students' first introduction to patterns. Therefore, it may take some students a while to recognize a pattern and to construct and extend patterns themselves. By having many opportunities to compare patterns and non-patterns, extend a given pattern, and construct and describe their own patterns, students become comfortable with identifying, looking for, and making repeating patterns.

The work students do on repeating patterns in this unit lays the foundation for the pattern work they do in later grades. By identifying and creating repeating patterns in Kindergarten, students begin to develop an understanding of one kind of pattern, develop an awareness of patterns in mathematics, and begin to look for patterns that can help them understand important mathematical relationships.

Assessment: Repeating Patterns

By the end of this unit, students are expected to be able to copy, construct, and extend simple repeating patterns (Benchmark 1). Student may construct simple AB or ABC patterns or more complex patterns such as AAB or ABB patterns. Assessment Checklist: Repeating Patterns *(M3), is included to help you keep track of your observations about students' patterns over the course of this unit. What follows is a vignette from one teacher, describing what she has learned about students as she observed their work toward the end of Investigation 2.*

My kindergarteners have been working on the Pattern Unit for at least two weeks. Today I decided that I was not going to introduce any new ideas or activities to the whole class, but rather set up several places around the classroom where students could work independently or in pairs to construct and extend patterns. I set out familiar materials: connecting cubes, pattern blocks, color tiles, two-color counters, and arrow cards. My goal was to observe as much as possible today so that I could get a better feel for the understandings my students were developing around the ideas of pattern. I thought I needed this time for them to solidify ideas and for me to figure out the next steps based on what they needed.

Connecting Cubes *When I joined these four students, I noticed that though they were talking as they worked, they were each working independently on their own ideas. Sarah was in the process of collecting as many red and yellow cubes as she could. I heard her say to the others, "I need lots of red and yellow ones." Timothy replied, "I need red too. And blue and green."*

Jennifer was snapping away. She had constructed a train of about 15 cubes. I noted that there was no distinguishable pattern to her work. I decided to come back later to check in. At that point, I put a note next to her name on my assessment checklist: Jennifer—random colors.

Russell was verbalizing to himself as he added each new piece to his pattern: "orange, black, orange, black, orange, black." I watched for a moment as he then made a change: "now blue, white, blue, white." Russell seemed to be changing color in midstream, though each part of his growing train of cubes followed a distinguishable AB pattern. Again, I made a note: Russell—two AB patterns connected as one.

Pattern Blocks *Jae and Latoya were well on their way when I came by to see their work. Jae had three different patterns laid out in front of him. They each contained eight pieces. They were all AB patterns. I made note of this for my records. I paused and asked whether he could tell me about his work. "I made three different patterns. One is square, triangle, square, triangle. This one is red, yellow, red, yellow. This one is big diamond, little diamond. See, they go over and over."*

I added to my notes that Jae used color, shape, and size to describe his patterns. I was curious about why he did this but did not want to stop too long.

Latoya had her pattern blocks standing up like a wall. She was struggling with ways to have them fit. She had three different pairs with a hexagon and a rhombus (known in my class as the blue diamond). Two pieces fit together the way she wanted them to. When she tried to connect them to follow her presumed pattern, they did not. It was interesting that she made pairs first and then tried to connect them. She was constructing the units first and then putting them together in a pattern. But she was struggling to make them into a wall.

I watched for a few minutes and then heard Jae suggest, "Use this" (handing her a trapezoid). Latoya added the trapezoid next to the rhombus. "It fits," I heard her exclaim. She then added a trapezoid to each group and proceeded to make an ABC pattern for her connected wall.

"No, just use red and yellow," Jae suggested to Latoya. "Then it will be a pattern."

"What do you mean, Jae?" I interjected. "A pattern only has two," he responded. "Like mine," pointing to the three different AB patterns he had made.

"Let's look at Latoya's pattern block wall. Latoya, do you think you made a pattern?" I asked. "I wanted to have two but it didn't fit," she said. "Having three fits. I guess it makes a pattern because it goes yellow, blue, red, yellow, blue, red. When it goes over and over the same, it's a pattern."

"Jae, can you add on to Latoya's pattern block wall?" I probed. Jae stood a hexagon on end next to the trapezoid. He then added the rhombus and a trapezoid. "It can keep going like this, but I thought a pattern was like this" (pointing to his work).

"See whether you can try and make one of your own like Latoya did," I said, offering a new challenge for him to take on. As I moved on to another group, I made a note to challenge the class with this idea that a pattern can be more than AB.

Color Tiles *Manuel, Mia, and Jack were working together with color tiles. They had one very long path stretching across the rug. I noticed that they were trying to use all four colors in their pattern. It started red, yellow, green, blue, red, yellow green, blue. As it progressed, sometimes the colors did not follow this pattern.*

"Tell me about your work," I said. "We wanted to use all the colors," responded Jack. "We wanted to work as a team," added Mia.

"Can you work as a team to describe your pattern for me?" I asked. The three children began to chime in unison, "red, yellow, green, blue." They barely looked at their pattern train. They seemed to know the chant for their pattern but had not taken the time to scrutinize every piece as they laid it down. I made a note of this but decided not to intervene. I thought I could recreate this situation for the whole class, or at least small groups, to consider.

Two-Color Counters *Beth and Rebecca were working with the two-color counters. They had about 15 or so stretched out in a big line. When I approached them, it did not appear that they had made a pattern. They seemed to be flipping at random and then counting how many yellow or red they had. I asked whether I could take a turn.*

I arranged eight chips in an AB pattern, starting with red. "Beth, please add on to my pattern." Beth correctly placed a red after the last yellow. Rebecca then took a turn and added a yellow. They alternated turns for a bit. The pattern grew longer. I was pleased that they could add onto the pattern I had made. But I wondered whether either or both of the girls noticed that they were always placing the same color and whether they were using this fact to help them continue the pattern.

I decided to mix it up a bit. "May I take a turn?" I asked. The girls agreed. First, I tried placing a red chip next to a red. Both girls jumped right on this. "No," they seemed to say in unison, "it has to be yellow." "See, it goes red, yellow, red, yellow," Rebecca offered.

I corrected my error and we continued taking turns. Rebecca placed a yellow and then Beth a red. Next, I placed a yellow. Rebecca put down a yellow next to mine and then Beth put down a red. Neither one seemed to notice the two yellows side by side. After I put down the next yellow, Rebecca began to put down another yellow, but then stopped. "Wait, I always do yellow, but you did yellow and now there's going to be two yellows together. . . . And look, there are two yellows here!" she said.

We started back at the beginning of our pattern. When we got to the two yellows, Rebecca flipped one over to make a red in the correct location. The girls then realized they needed to keep flipping to make the pattern work.

I thought this exchange was very complicated. It seemed to have something to do with even and odd, but I did not want to go there. I was pleased that Rebecca and Beth could stick with this task and add on to my pattern. They seemed to have a sense of an AB pattern and could correct an error if needed.

Arrow Cards *Several kids selected the arrow cards. They were the newest material available and had that novel appeal. As I got closer, I noticed that several children had made AB patterns with the arrows pointing up and then down. A few children were trying different directions. They seemed to be having more difficulty. I made a note to check whether directionality was the problem or they were just trying out something new. One child had eight arrow cards all pointing in the same direction.*

"Tell me about your work," I said to Lionel. "It's like a big sign at the movies telling you to go in," he described." "Is the movie sign a pattern?" I asked. "It flashes on and off so I guess so," he answered. "Does your sign flash on and off?" I asked. "No, but I know it really does."

I was intrigued by Lionel's work. I am never sure whether children will accept an arrangement of all the same color, shape, size, or direction as a pattern. I think it is, but they seem to struggle with this notion. Here I thought Lionel was on to this idea of an AAA pattern, but instead his description indicates that he sees this as an AB pattern because the movie sign alternates on and off.

I was pleased with the range of work I saw today. A few students are still working on being able to construct a simple repeating pattern, but most students are comfortably making patterns with a variety of materials. I want to bring up with the whole class the possibility of there being patterns other than AB patterns and see what they think about it. There were a number of issues around pattern that I saw students work on such as figuring out what makes a pattern, describing a pattern in different ways, and correcting a mistake in a pattern. There is much to explore and learn about patterns.

Observing students as they work with different materials to create patterns provides a number of contexts to find out what students are understanding about repeating patterns and what aspects they are still working on. You may find that students who are unable to construct a repeating pattern themselves are able to continue a pattern started by someone else or are at least able to distinguish between patterns and non-patterns. Students who are easily creating AB patterns using a variety of colors, shapes, or materials may begin to generalize about these patterns and see that they are in fact the same. They can also be encouraged to construct more complex patterns. Use the notes you take on Assessment Checklist: Repeating Patterns (M3) to help you distinguish what students are understanding about patterns and what might be next steps for them.

Assessment Checklist: Repeating Patterns

Student	Kinds of patterns students construct	Copy/extend a pattern type	Notes
Jennifer	cubes—not a pattern—random colors		
Russell	cubes—2 AB patterns connected as one		
Jae	pattern blocks 3 patterns, all AB		described using color for one, size for one and shape for one—thinks only AB is a pattern?
Latoya	pattern blocks wall—at first AB, then ABC		makes units first then puts in pattern
Beth		two-color counters—extends AB	recognizes mistake in pattern & corrects
Rebecca		two-color counters—extends AB	recognizes mistake in pattern & corrects
Manuel, Mia & Jack	ABCD—color tiles		long, describes a pattern correctly but mistakes in constructed pattern

What's the Unit?

Consider this pattern: red–yellow–yellow–red–yellow–yellow–red–yellow–yellow. We can decompose this repeating pattern into the sections that recur. In so doing, we determine the unit of the pattern, which, in this case, is red–yellow–yellow. Being able to see which elements repeat, as well as the relationships that exist between elements in the pattern, are important mathematical ideas that challenge many kindergarteners.

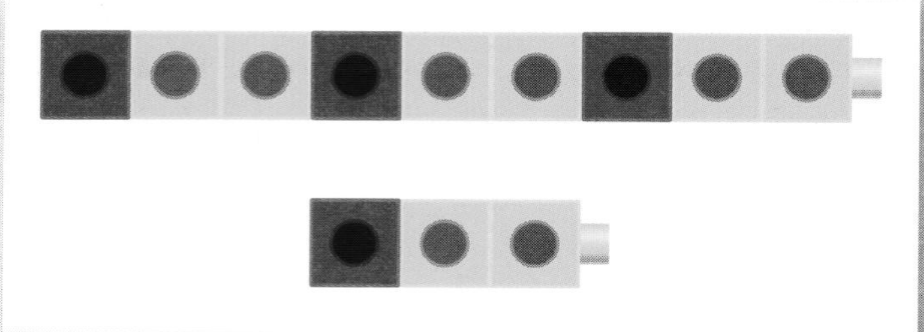

In the game, *Break the Train,* students encounter the idea of a pattern unit. They are asked to decompose pattern "trains" into "cars," or the units that make-up the pattern. For example, if one student builds a red–blue–red–blue–red–blue train of 12 cubes, her partner's task is to break the train apart into six individual red–blue train cars, in order to highlight the repeating units of the pattern.

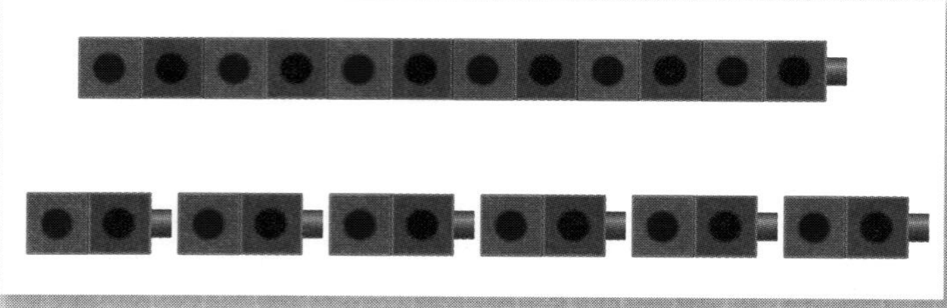

Initially, when students are working with AB pattern trains and cars of just two cubes, this task may seem easy. However, as students begin to work with more complex patterns, such as AAB or ABB, it is not uncommon to see them continue to break the trains into sections of two cubes rather than into complete units of three cubes. For these students, recognizing the unit of an AB or even an ABC pattern is easier than finding the unit in AAB or ABB patterns. As they gain experience and become familiar with more complex patterns, they will bring this understanding to their knowledge of how patterns work.

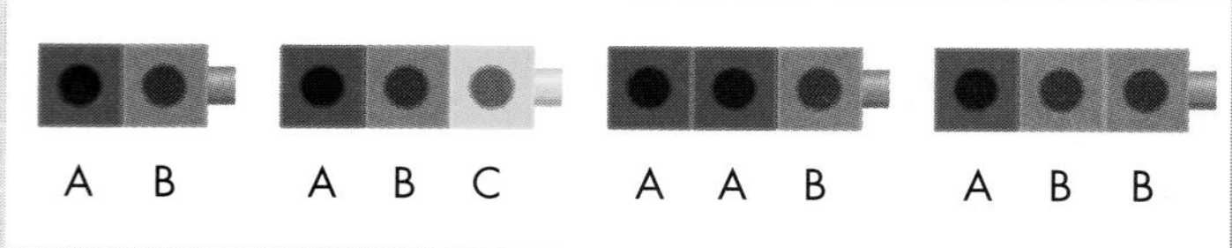

You may find that you need to offer students multiple opportunities to experience the activities in this Investigation as they begin to think about patterns in new ways.

Break the Train

In the game, *Break the Train,* students construct repeating pattern trains and then decompose their partners' pattern trains into "cars," or units. Dennis and Carmen have each constructed a pattern train from cubes. The teacher watches as they begin to break them into cars.

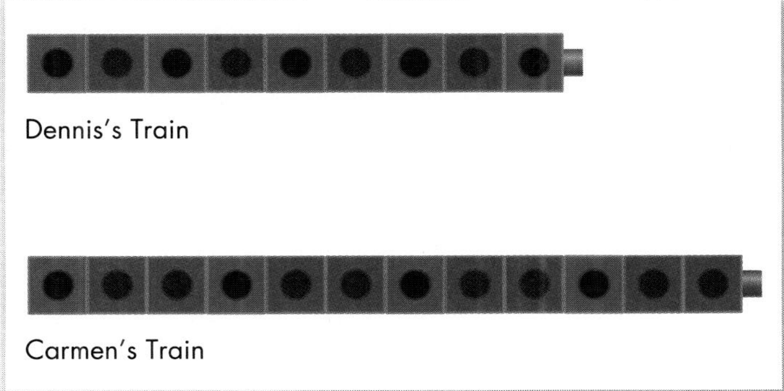

Dennis: [Holds Carmen's pattern train next to his.] They look the same, but yours is longer.

Carmen: That's OK. You go.

Dennis: Hmm. . .

Dennis removes the last two (blue–blue) cubes from the train and leaves them connected to each other. He unsnaps the next two cubes (*blue–green*) in the same way and repeats this step until the train is broken into six "cars" as follows: green–blue; blue–green; blue–blue; green–blue; blue–green; blue–blue.

Dennis: I did it!

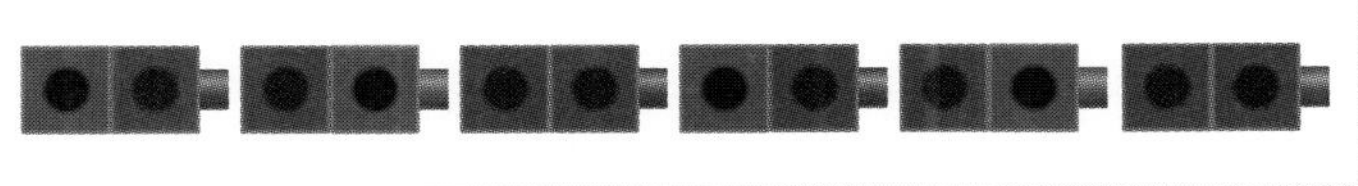

Carmen: OK, it's my turn. Yours is like a candy cane but with green and blue. Green, then blue, green then blue. [Unsnaps the cubes until she has four sets of green–blue cars and a single green cube.] You missed one. [Adds another blue to make a complete car.]

Dennis: No [unsnaps this blue cube]. I want green at the end.

Carmen: But it has to be the same. You have to have green and blue to make the pattern.

Dennis: No, you can make it like I did. It's still a pattern.

Teacher: Can you tell me what's going on?

Dennis: I don't want blue at the end. I want green.

Carmen: That's not right. You have to have the same. The cars have to be the same. I made four green and blue cars and then one green. I need a blue.

Dennis: But I want to have green at the end.

Teacher: I can see that you want your pattern to end with a green cube. Can you put in your own words what Carmen is trying to say?

Dennis: She wants a blue, too, so it's the same.

Teacher: What do you mean by *the same?*

Dennis: The same green–blue over and over. But I want green at the end.

Teacher: Carmen, is that what you mean, that you want the same green–blue, over and over?

Carmen: Yes, that's when it's a pattern. You have to have the same go over and over and over and over.

Dennis: It does. Green–blue, green–blue, over and over.

Teacher: Let's look at the pattern train that Carmen made. I see that Dennis has broken it into parts. Dennis, can you tell me about your work?

Dennis: I made six of them; four are green and blue and two are blue and blue.

Teacher: Carmen do you agree with how Dennis broke your train?

Carmen: No. They are not the same. He has green-blue and blue–green and blue–blue.

Dennis: That's the same, green and blue.

Carmen: No, this is green and blue, and this is blue and green. They're not the same. See, here is green first and here is blue first, and I thought there would be three over and over.

Teacher: What do you mean?

Carmen: My pattern was green–blue–blue, green–blue–blue.

Teacher: Dennis, please put Carmen's train back together. [Dennis resnaps the cubes.] Carmen, is this what your pattern looked like?

Carmen: Yes.

Teacher: Dennis, please break Carmen's train again. Try to think about what she said about her pattern.

Dennis: [Looks closely at Carmen's train.] She said three. So, green and blue and one more blue is three [unsnaps the first three cubes and continues to successfully break Carmen's train]. Oh, I see. Now they're the same. She made cars with three. Can you do that?

Teacher: What do you think?

Dennis: I guess so.

Carmen: I think you can. It's a pattern. It goes over and over. It's just three over and over.

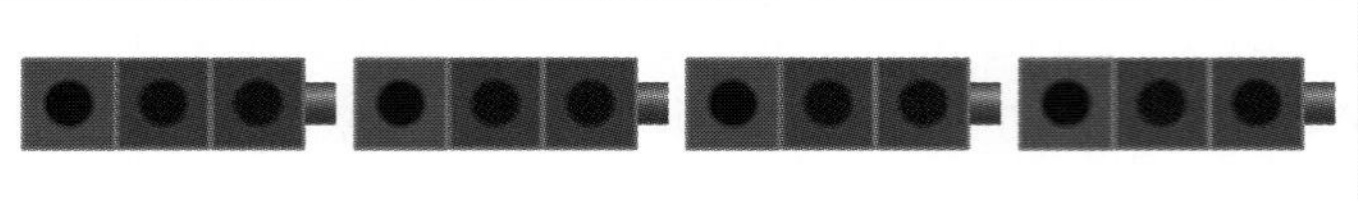

The teacher observes the students carefully as they break each other's trains into units. She decides to intervene when the students cannot agree over whether it is OK for Dennis' train to end in green. Although this disagreement is not resolved, they are able to articulate why they think it can or cannot end in green.

The teacher then asks the pair to look carefully at the way Dennis has broken Carmen's train into units. By having Dennis put the train back together and listen to Carmen describe her repeating pattern, Dennis is then able to correctly break the train into units. Dennis leaves the conversation seemingly with a clearer understanding of what it means to break a repeating pattern into units and perhaps a broader understanding of repeating patterns.

Dialogue Box

Two Arrangements of Color

In Session 1.4 students discuss two different cube trains, one with colors arranged in a repeating AB patten and the other with assorted colors in an arrangement that does not repeat. The teacher is interested in seeing how students will describe and compare the two trains and whether any students use the word *pattern* to describe the arrangement of colors that repeats. To learn more about what they are thinking, the teacher encourages students to explain their observations.

Teacher: What do you see in this train [holds up the train with assorted colors]?

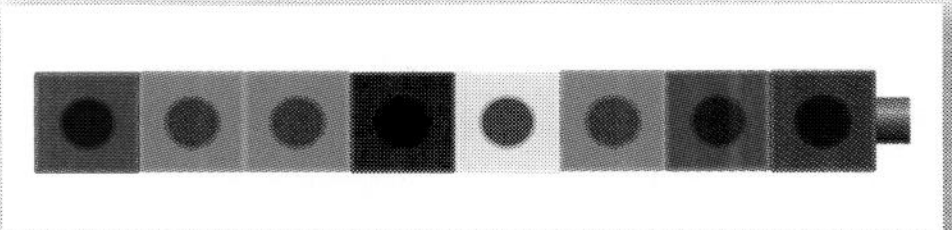

Timothy: It looks like a rainbow.

Rebecca: No. Rainbows don't have black and white.

Mia: I see eight squares.

Lionel: They make a train. See, each block is like a car. The red is the engine. The brown is the caboose.

Jason: I see that too, but I think there are nine cars.

Teacher: Raise your hand if you were thinking about the number of cubes I'm holding. . . . I see that some of you were thinking about the number. Let's count them together.

All students: 1, 2, 3, 4, 5, 6, 7, 8.

Mia: Yup, there's eight.

Lionel: Eight cars in the train!

Teacher: Now look at this other train [points to the train with alternating colors].

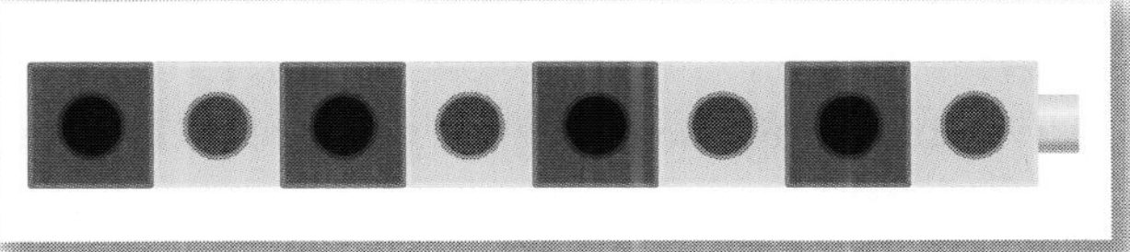

Tammy: It has only two colors.

Abby: I see red and yellow, red and yellow.

Mia: It still has eight.

Lionel: It's still a train with eight cars.

Manuel: It's like my shirt. [He is wearing a checkerboard flannel shirt.]

Kiyo: It goes red, yellow, red, yellow, red, yellow, red, yellow. [She points to the cubes the teacher is holding, moving her finger from left to right as she says each new color and goes on to the next cube in the train.]

Teacher: How would you compare these two trains? What's the same, and what's different?

Hugo: That one has a lot of colors. That one has only two colors.

Cindy: I think this [points to the red and yellow train] is a pattern.

Teacher: What do you mean it is a pattern?

Cindy: A pattern keeps going over and over. See red, yellow, red, yellow. The other one isn't a pattern because it's just colors.

Raul: One is pretty and one is striped.

Teacher: Can you tell us more about what you mean?

Raul: I think this one is pretty [picks up the train with multiple colors]. It has lots of colors. It has my favorite color green. This one [reaches for the second train] has stripes. It goes red, yellow, red, yellow . . .

Emma: One is a rainbow and one is a candy cane.

Teacher: Cindy has used the word *pattern* to describe this type of arrangement. We are going to be learning a lot about repeating patterns in the next few weeks. This [holds up the red and yellow train] is a repeating pattern, and this [holds up the train with assorted colors] is not a repeating pattern. Has anyone else ever heard the word *pattern*?

The students in this class have found many ways to describe and compare the two cube trains. They find their own ways of describing the trains and what distinguishes one from the other. They say one has "a lot of colors" and is "like a rainbow." The other one "has stripes," is "like a candy cane," and "goes red, yellow, red, yellow, red, yellow." Most 5- and 6-year-olds are not familiar with the word *pattern*. If they are, they have a very limited understanding of its meaning. Now that the term has come up in discussion, the teacher will model its use as the class does the rest of the activities in this unit.

Sharing Our Cube Trains

In Session 1.4 after comparing two cube trains, students construct their own cube trains and then bring one to a discussion. During the discussion, they group the cube trains and talk about what is similar among all of the cube trains in the group.

Ricardo: I made mine just like the rainbow one, but I used purple.

Jennifer: I made mine with only two colors. See, black and white like a zebra.

Latoya: I used two colors, blue and yellow.

Teacher: I notice that several of you used just two colors. Let's put those together in a pile so we can look at them more closely. Let's also make a pile of those with more than two colors. Will we need any other piles? (*The class agrees that two piles will work.*) Is there anything we can say about the two piles? What do you notice?

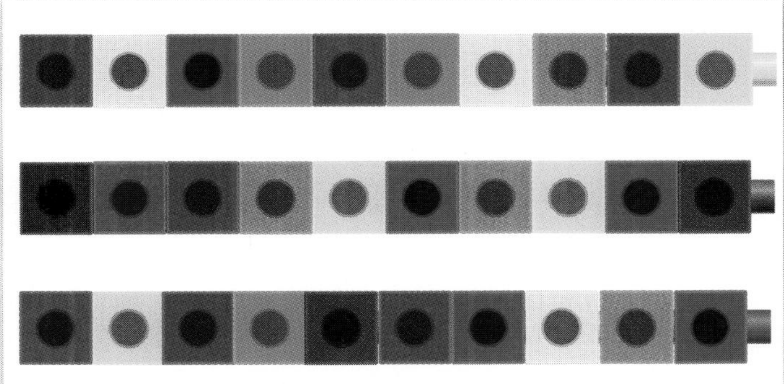

Victor: More kids used rainbow colors.

Carmen: Lots of kids made red and white ones like candy canes.

Teacher: Let's look at just one pile at a time. What do you notice about these? [Points to train with assorted colors.]

Raul: I like the rainbow ones. They're pretty.

Kyle: They are all different colors.

Teacher: Now let's look at these [points to the other pile]. What do you notice?

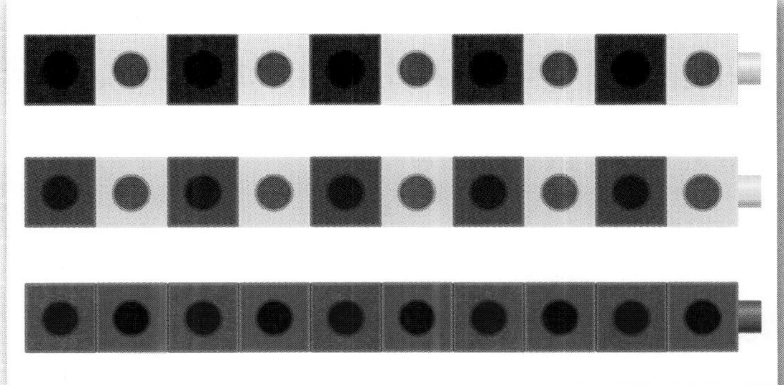

Yoshio: They look like stripes.

Timothy: They look like a funny checkerboard.

Carmen: Some of us made the same. There are a lot of candy canes.

Emma: These are all patterns. Well, this one isn't [picks up a train that is red, white, red, white, red, white, white, red].

Teacher: Can you make it a pattern?

Emma: [Changes the order of the last two cubes.] Now it is. See, red, white, red, white.

Teacher: Emma just changed the order of some of the cubes. What do other people think? Does that make sense to you?

Kaitlyn: I think it looks better now.

Brad: That was mine. I meant to do that. I meant it to go red, white, red, white all the way down. I just missed.

Teacher: What is it about this train that makes everyone so sure that the last two blocks should be turned around?

Carmen: It makes the candy cane.

Jack: You just know it has to be that way. Red, white, red, white, over and over and over.

Teacher: It sure does go over and over! Which trains here go over and over and over? (The class agrees that all of the trains in the second pile go "over and over.") Which arrangements make it easy to tell what comes next?

Carmen: These do [points to the second pile]. They're stripes. [Picks up a red and white train.] You can see that white comes after red every time.

Jennifer: You can always tell which color comes next by looking for that color. Then it has to be the other one.

Teacher: What about these? [Points to the other pile.]

Yoshio: No, they are just different colors.

Emma: They could be any color.

Carmen: They don't make stripes.

Jennifer: You can't tell what comes next after black here [picks up one non-repeating arrangement ending in black] because there is no other black. How would you know?

Everyone agrees that the assorted colors do not help you know what comes next and that the alternating colors do. In this discussion, the teacher helped students focus on the attributes of a repeating pattern by offering them a structure for sorting the trains and asking them to compare and contrast them. Although most students did not leave the discussion with a clear understanding of *pattern,* the foundation for future work and for future conversations was established.

What Might Come Next?

As students look again at two arrangements of colored cubes—one in a repeating pattern and one in a non-repeating arrangement of assorted colors—they are asked to hold up a cube showing what color they think comes next in each arrangement. Students begin with an assorted arrangement (red, white, yellow, black, blue, orange, green, brown) and try to determine what color would come after the brown cube.

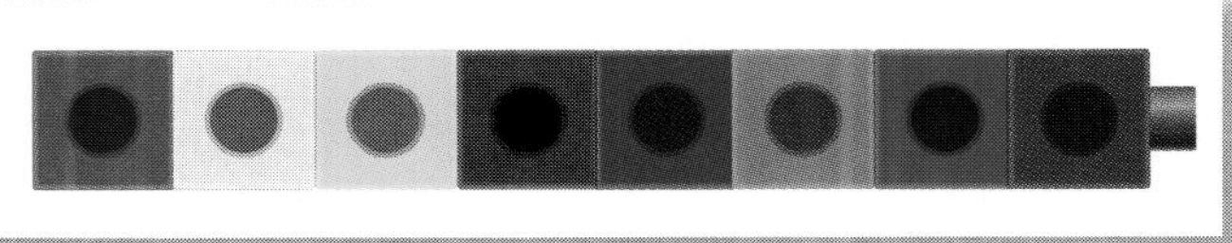

Corey: I think pink. I like pink, and it's not there.

Sarah: No, red. See, it will start over.

Jack: [Looking at his cubes on the floor in front of him] It could be any color. It doesn't need to start over. That's boring.

Abby: I don't know what goes here [points to the brown end], but I think white goes here [she snaps her white cube to the left of the red cube].

Teacher: Why do you think white goes here?

Abby: Because now it will go white, red, white, just like the other one.

Teacher: It is interesting to think of what might go here (points to the cube Abby has added to the arrangement), but I don't want to forget what the original train looks like, so I'm going to take this off and give you the white cube back. [Redirects the focus to the other end of the train.] Any other ideas of what goes here? I see that Jason is showing a yellow cube.

Jason: I like yellow.

After everyone had a chance to share his or her ideas, the teacher directed attention to the alternating red–white arrangement.

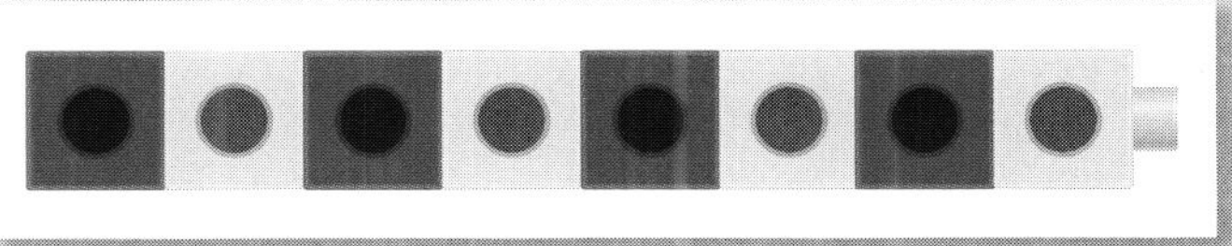

Teacher: What might go here? Any ideas? Hold up one of the cubes from your cup to show which color you think comes next.

Ricardo: I think it is going to be a red.

Tammy: Me too.

Kiyo: Not a red, a white.

Victor: Yeah, white.

Timothy: But I want it to be blue like the flag. See, red, white, and blue! [Points to the flag hanging near the meeting area.]

Ricardo: But it has to be red.

Kiyo: Or white!

Teacher: Many of you are holding up a red or white cube. Why do you think it would be red or white?

Victor: Because it has to be red, white, red, white . . .

Ricardo: Yes, it's got to be!

Teacher: When we looked at the first arrangement, we had a lot of different ideas. For this arrangement, we seem to have just three ideas. Why is this? Who has an idea?

Hugo: The first one could be any colors. The second one can be only red or white. It's easy to tell what comes next because it has to be red or white. That's all.

Tammy: Yeah, red or white. The first one could be anything, even a color we don't know.

Sarah: But we could start the rainbow one over. [Points to the first train.] You could make this a pattern by starting over with red.

Brad: But it's not a pattern now. Just the candy cane is a pattern. You can always tell what will come next.

Teacher: Some of you are thinking about how the red–white pattern repeats. If it keeps repeating in the same way, you can always tell what comes next. This is important to think about. We could make the first group of cubes, the rainbow one, into a repeating pattern like Sarah said, but it would have to start over.

In this discussion students try to figure out which color cube will come next in two different cube trains and explain why they think so. By trying to determine what comes next in a cube train that is a non-repeating arrangement of colors and trying to determine what comes next in a cube train that is an AB pattern, the students in this class are beginning to think about the predictable nature of repeating patterns. The teacher highlights this by pointing out that students had many different ideas about what might come next in the non-repeating cube train, but only three ideas about what they thought would come next in the patterned cube train, and by asking them why they think this might be.

Dialogue Box

I Think It's Green

The teacher in this class has created a repeating pattern with color tiles in a pocket chart and has covered the last few color tiles with cards with question marks on them. The students describe the pattern and try to determine the colors of the tiles hidden by the question mark cards.

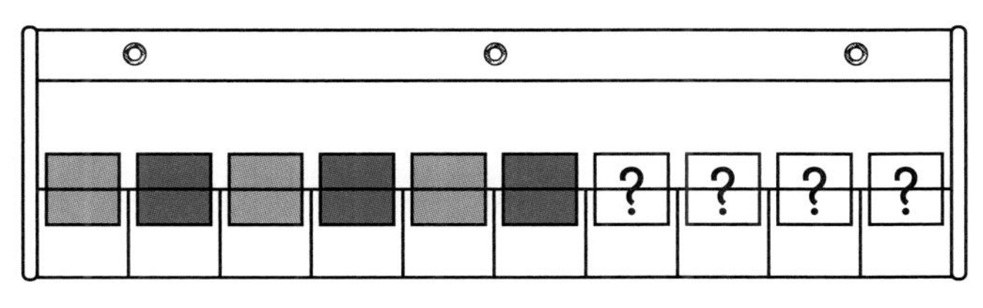

Teacher: I have made pattern in this the pocket chart. What do you notice?

Hugo: (Points to the question mark.) What's that?

Kyle: It's like a fishhook, only it's upside down.

Latoya: Look, it's over here, too. [She points to the end mark on a poster that says "How Many Days Have We Been in School?"]

Sarah: And, it's in books, too.

Teacher: I think we can find this symbol in lots of places. What do you think it means?

Jennifer: I don't know.

Kyle: We could turn it over and pretend to catch something.

Kaitlyn: Maybe we are supposed to guess the next one.

Raul: Yes, like a pattern . . . green, blue, green, blue, green. Green goes next.

Sarah: In books it means you have a question. It's called an explanation mark. That's what my mom said when we read.

Teacher: You all have lots of ideas. It is used in books, and it does mean you are asking a question. It is called a question mark. When Kaitlyn said that maybe we are supposed to guess a color, that is what I was thinking when I put the question mark cards in the pocket chart. When Kyle said it looks like an upside-down fishhook, I realized I had never thought of it like that before. It is like an upside-down fishhook.

Teacher: Now see whether you can add on to this repeating pattern. If the pattern continues to repeat in the same way, can you figure out what color is under each of the question marks? Hold up the color you think will be next. Why do you think so?

Mia: I think it will be green. See green–blue, green–blue. It has to be.

Tammy: I think it will be green, too.

Jason: I think it will be blue.

Victor: No, it has to be green.

Jason: It doesn't have to be green. It can be blue. I like blue. I want there to be two blues.

Teacher: Victor, why do you think it is green?

Victor: Because that's the way it goes: green–blue, green–blue.

Teacher: Jason, why do you think it is blue?

Jason: I like blue. I want there to be more blues.

Teacher: Having favorite colors is important, but remember that you are trying to predict what comes next in a repeating pattern. What does the pattern tell you so far? Let's say it together.

Everyone: Green–blue, green–blue.

Jason: I guess it will be green. Even though I wish it were blue.

Teacher: What makes you think so?

Jason: Because green comes after blue.

When asked to determine what comes next in the repeating pattern, most of the students agree that the next color will be green, but one student has a different idea. The teacher asks a few students to explain why they think the color they chose would be next. When the student who thinks the next color will be blue says it is his favorite color, the teacher acknowledges that fact but then helps the students focus on using what they already know to figure this out. The student then confirms it will be green. He demonstrates his newfound understanding of the repeating nature of this arrangement by stating, "Because green comes after blue."

Dialogue Box

A "Harder" Pattern

During Math Workshop some students are playing *What Comes Next?* In this game, Player 1 creates a repeating pattern and covers the last few items with cups. Then, Player 2 copies the part of the pattern that is visible and tries to figure out what is underneath the cups. Player 1 reveals what is under the cup after Player 2 adds a tile to her pattern to show what color she thinks is beneath the cup. When one pair disagrees on what comes next, the teacher intervenes.

Manuel: I'm going to go first. I'll make the pattern and you can guess.

Corey: Okay.

Corey buries her head in her arms on the table. Manuel constructs a red–yellow repeating pattern with 12 tiles and covers the last eight tiles with cups.

Manuel: I'm ready.

Corey: Okay, now I can start building your pattern. [She lays out four matching tiles of red–yellow–red–yellow.]

Manuel: (Points to the first cup.) What comes next?

Corey: That's easy. Red. [She adds a red to her pattern, and Manuel removes the cup, showing a red color tile. The game continues quickly until all of the tiles have been uncovered.]

Corey: Now it's my turn. Close your eyes. I'm going to make it harder. [Using the unit red–yellow–yellow, she forms an ABB pattern with 12 tiles and covers the last ten with cups, leaving only red–yellow showing.] I'm ready.

Manuel: That's not hard. [He puts out red–yellow, and continues to build red–yellow–red–yellow until he has 12 tiles in his pattern.]

Corey: (Giggling) Nope!

Manuel: It has to be.

Corey: No, it doesn't.

Manuel: Yes, it does.

[The students continue to argue as the teacher approaches.]

Teacher: What's going on?

Students play What Comes Next?

Manuel: She made a red–yellow pattern, so I think red goes next. See, I made the pattern, too.

Corey: But that's not right.

Manuel: It has to be!

Teacher: Let me look more closely at the work both of you have done. This is Corey's pattern? [Points to the path where ten cups cover the tiles.] And this is what Manuel thinks will come next? (The students agree.) Let's go back a step. What goes here? [Points to the first cup.]

Manuel: You have red–yellow, so I made a red–yellow pattern. I think it will be red.

Teacher: Corey, show us what you have next in your pattern.

Corey: Okay [removes the cup]. See, it's yellow, not red. (Manuel looks very frustrated.)

Teacher: Manuel, now you can see more of Corey's pattern. What do you think now?

Manuel: [After a long pause] I get it.

Manuel begins to remove color tiles from the path he built until he has only three tiles red–yellow–yellow.

Teacher: What do you think comes next?

Manuel: I don't know.

Teacher: Corey, show the next piece in your pattern.

This continues until six pieces of the pattern are revealed: red–yellow–yellow–red–yellow–yellow.

Manuel: I get it now. [He lays out six more tiles, making the red–yellow–yellow pattern.]

Teacher: Are you sure?

Manuel: I think so.

Teacher: Corey, show us the rest of your pattern and see if Manuel's matches now.

Corey: It does. See, I told you I was going to make it hard!

Teacher: Yes, you did. What made it so hard?

Corey: I made a pattern with one red and two yellows.

Teacher: Yes, that kind of pattern is tricky, but I see another reason why it was so hard. Manuel, why was this one so hard?

Manuel: It wasn't fair. When it was just red and yellow, anything could go next.

Teacher: It did not seem fair to you. Do you think the way Corey showed you only a little piece of the pattern is what made it so hard?

Manuel: Yes!

Teacher: Deciding what comes next in a repeating pattern is hard work. You need to have enough information so you can be sure about what comes next. This was a good example of how hard it can be. Can I show this to the class later so we can talk about this? [Manuel and Corey nod their heads.]

As these students play *What Comes Next?* the issue of how much information is needed to correctly determine what will come next in a repeating pattern is revealed. When Manuel finds it hard to determine the next color in the pattern, the teacher helps the two students realize that figuring out what comes next in this situation was not only difficult because Corey constructed a challenging pattern, but because Manuel did not have enough information. As Manuel stated, "when it was just red and yellow, anything could go next."

Student Math Handbook Flip Chart

The *Student Math Handbook Flip Chart* pages related to this unit are pictured on the following pages.

Math Words and Ideas | Read Together

Patterns All Around Us

Look at these patterns.

What do you notice about these patterns? Do you see any patterns around you?

Note to Teacher: ***What Comes Next?*** **Session 1.1.** This page includes a variety of patterns. Ask students to describe the images and to explain why they think each is or is not a pattern.

thirty-nine SMH 39

Math Words and Ideas, p. 39

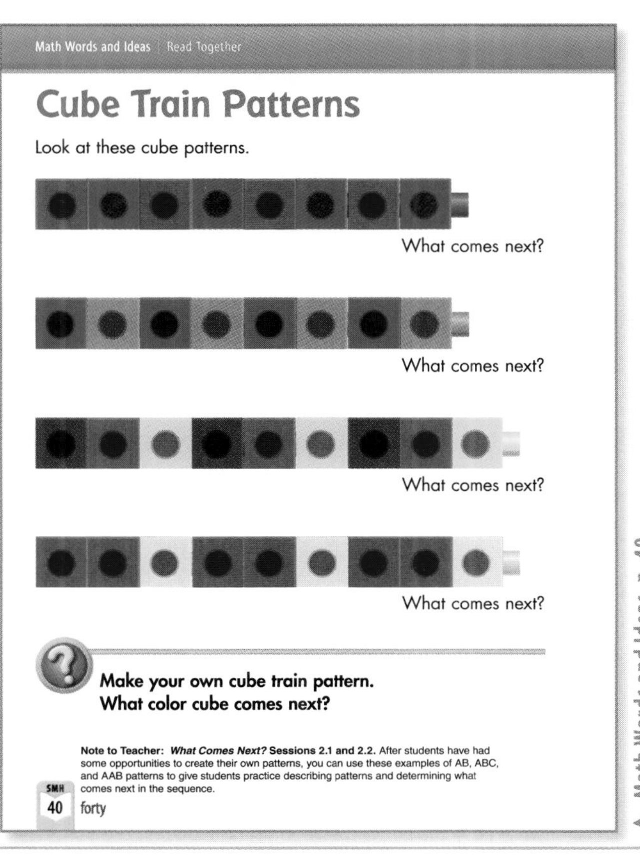

Math Words and Ideas | Read Together

Cube Train Patterns

Look at these cube patterns.

What comes next?

What comes next?

What comes next?

What comes next?

Make your own cube train pattern. What color cube comes next?

Note to Teacher: ***What Comes Next?*** **Sessions 2.1 and 2.2.** After students have had some opportunities to create their own patterns, you can use these examples of AB, ABC, and AAB patterns to give students practice describing patterns and determining what comes next in the sequence.

SMH 40 forty

Math Words and Ideas, p. 40

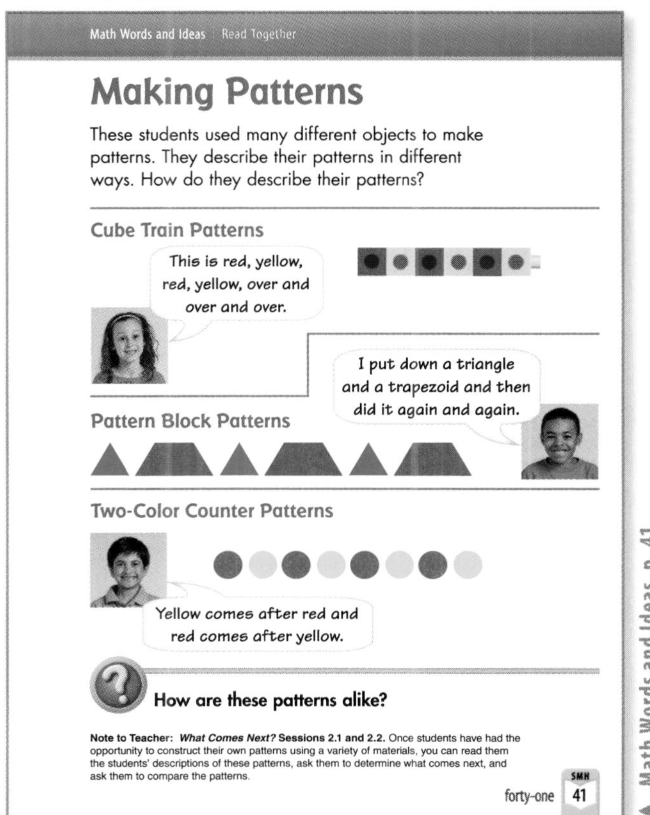

Math Words and Ideas | Read Together

Making Patterns

These students used many different objects to make patterns. They describe their patterns in different ways. How do they describe their patterns?

Cube Train Patterns

This is red, yellow, red, yellow, over and over and over.

Pattern Block Patterns

I put down a triangle and a trapezoid and then did it again and again.

Two-Color Counter Patterns

Yellow comes after red and red comes after yellow.

How are these patterns alike?

Note to Teacher: ***What Comes Next?*** **Sessions 2.1 and 2.2.** Once students have had the opportunity to construct their own patterns using a variety of materials, you can read them the students' descriptions of these patterns, ask them to determine what comes next, and ask them to compare the patterns.

forty-one SMH 41

Math Words and Ideas, p. 41

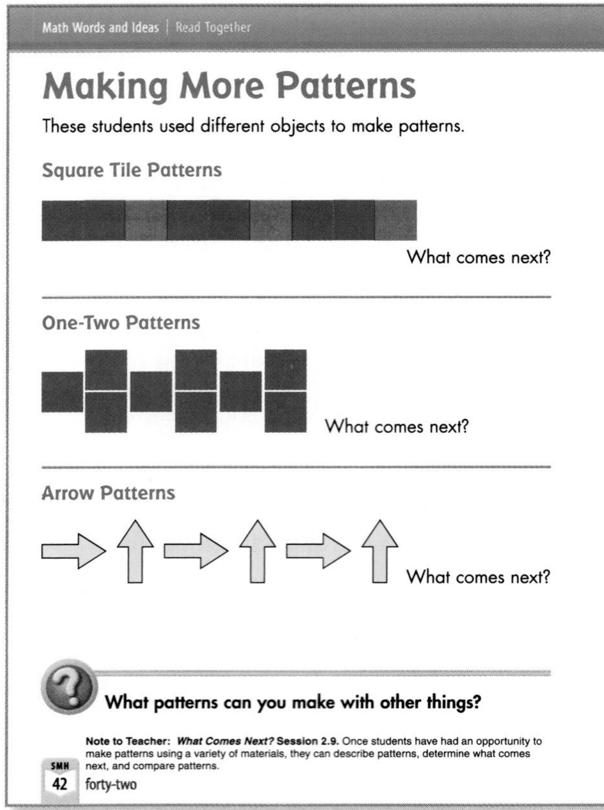

Math Words and Ideas, p. 42

Math Words and Ideas, p. 43

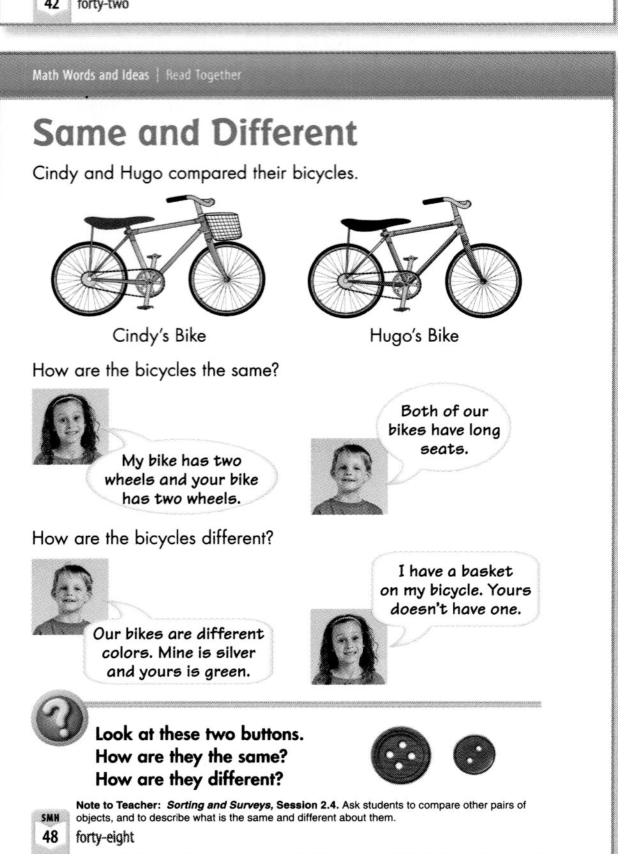

Math Words and Ideas, p. 48

Index

IN THIS UNIT